TAP!
TAP!
ROGER'S TAGGING DEVICE.

D. C. Thomson & Co., 185 Fleet Street, London EC4A 2HS.
ISBN 0-85116-556-7

SSSSSH!
DENNIS the MENACE and GNASHER
CLICK CLICK
ROLL
RUMBLE!
RUMBLE!
GNASH! GNASH! GNASH!
OH, NO! DONE IT NOW, GNASHER!
TRIP
TUG
GNEEK!
THERE'S NO PLACE TO HIDE!
YIKES!
ROLL ROLL
ZOOM
RUMBLE
GASP! IS THIS THE END OF DENNIS AND GNASHER?

HO-HO! WELL DONE, GNASHER! QUICK THINKING TO GNASH HOLES OUT OF THE PLASTER WALL!
ZOOM!
ZOOM!
RUMBLE!
At the end of the hall—
SAFE
WE'VE MADE IT TO THE SAFE. CAN YOU DO ANYTHING TO OPEN THE STEEL DOOR?
I'LL SHOW YOU THE AMAZING EFFECT A MENACE JUMPER CAN HAVE!
SNORE! GRUNT!
Dennis's Dad.
SNORE!
TUG
So—
THE CHANGE BEGINS WITH A MEANCE HAIR STYLE!
PING
PING
PYOING
MENACE SHORTS APPEAR!
PYOING
ZOOM
ZOOM

GNASH!
GNASH!
GNASH!
SAFE
CHORTLE! SILLY QUESTION!
VERY MENACING THINGS — MY JUMPERS!
SAFE
GRAB
I'LL TAKE ONE!
MENACE JUMPERS KEEP OUT
EASY DOES IT, GNASHER!
Until—
COME ON— LET'S MENACE!
HA-HA! MENACING KNEES, NOW!
POP
POP
SEE! ONE OF MY JUMPERS IS SO POWERFUL, IT CAN CHANGE MY DAD INTO A MENACE!
LEAP
GNEESH!

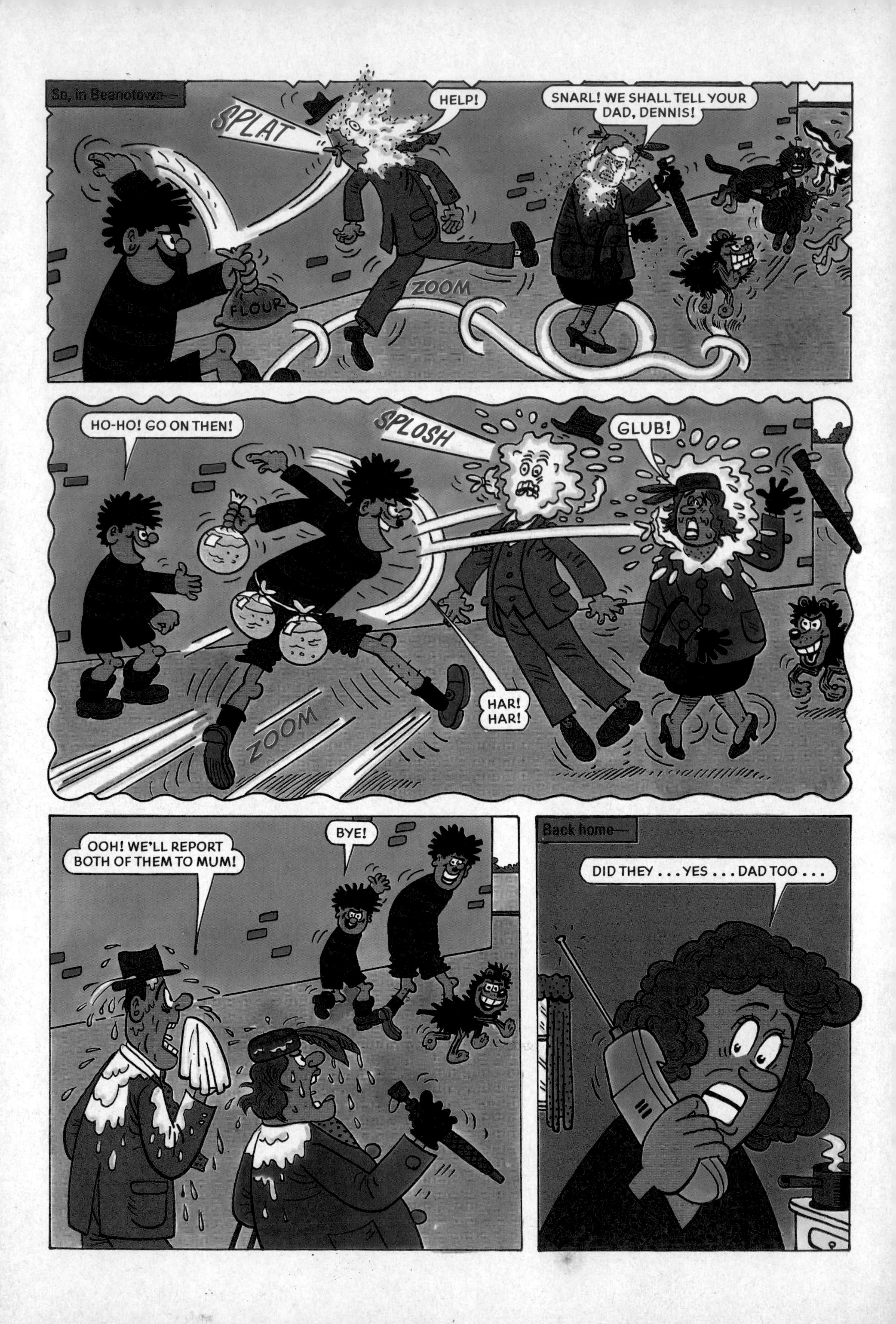
So, in Beanotown—
SPLAT
HELP!
SNARL! WE SHALL TELL YOUR DAD, DENNIS!
FLOUR
ZOOM
HO-HO! GO ON THEN!
SPLOSH
GLUB!
HAR! HAR!
ZOOM
OOH! WE'LL REPORT BOTH OF THEM TO MUM!
BYE!
Back home—
DID THEY . . . YES . . . DAD TOO . . .

Soon—
I'LL HAVE TO SORT THIS OUT!

WHAT A SUPER MENACE YOU ARE, DAD!
CHORTLE! THANK YOU, SON!
GNASH!

GOOD! HERE COME THE MENACES!
RIP

TAKE THAT!
DROP

GOOD! DAD'S SUIT JACKET WILL MAKE HIM 'DAD' AGAIN!
PING
PING
PING

GASP!
COME HERE, YOU MENACE!
EH?
GRAB
OH, NO! I MISSED DAD AND THE JACKET LANDED ON DENNIS!
GNEH?
. . . NO POCKET MONEY FOR A MONTH . . . WASH YOUR NECK EVERY DAY . . . NAG . . . NAG . . .
PUSH
HO-HO! DON'T WORRY, READERS. I HAVE A SPARE SUIT JACKET AND MENACE JUMPER BACK HOME TO CHANGE THEM BACK TO 'DENNIS' AND 'DAD'!

The BEANO BIRDS
BRR! IT'S F-FREEZING IN MY NEST.
SHIVER!
CHATTER!
Suddenly—
MIAOW! COME TO KITTY, MY PRETTY!
But—
GRAB!
MEAH! MISSED!
WHOOOSH!
HOVER!
NASTY CAT! I'LL PAY IT BACK!
LEAP!
ZOOOM!
PECK! PECK! PECK!
MEE-ERK!
I'VE GOT A LOVELY, WARM, FURRY, NEST NOW . . .
SNUG!
. . . AND THAT CAT'S THE LAUGHING STOCK OF THE NEIGHBOURHOOD.
EXTREMELY EMBARRASSED!
MEE-HEE-HEE!
PURR-HURR!
DODGE BOOK

BALL BOY
HMM! LOOKS COLD AND WINDY OUT THERE — AND I'M IN GOAL TODAY.
SO, I'LL WEAR THESE HOT WATER BOTTLES AS WELL AS MY TRACK SUIT.
AND SOME FAN HEATERS NEXT TO THE GOALS.
WAHEY! THIS MAKES DIVING FOR BALLS EASY.
BOUNCE!
Then —
OOPS! THAT BOUNCING HAS MADE MY BOTTLES SPRING A LEAK.

AND THE LEAK HAS MADE MY GOALMOUTH MUDDY.
VERY MUDDY TO DIVE INTO.
OH-OH! FORGOT ABOUT THOSE HEATERS.
BLAST OF HEAT!
THEY'VE DRIED THE MUD — I CAN'T MOVE AT ALL!
HARD
HARD
BAH! WHAT'S THE USE OF A GOALIE WHO CAN'T MOVE?
PLENTY, IF HE LOOKS LIKE A MONSTER FROM OUTER SPACE.
TRUE ENOUGH!
WAH!
HE'S HORRIBLE!
RUN!

BIFF

BASH STREET
From the picture clues given, guess what the
1 LIGHT RAIN
2
SHIVER
3
4
5
1 TON
1 TON
1 TON

WEATHER REPORT
...eather's like in The Bash Street Area. (The first one's done for you.)
JAIL
6
7
CLAP!
8
9
BURP!
OLIVE
RADISH
BEANS
SMASH!
10
ANSWERS
1. Light rain. 2. Thick Mist. 3. Cold front. 4. Bright sunshine. 5. Heavy showers. 6. Outbreaks of snow. 7. Thunder claps. 8. Icy blast. 9. Strong winds. 10. Broken clouds

MINNIE the MINX
Holiday time!
HURRY UP, MINNIE! TIME TO LEAVE!
OKAY, DAD!
WHUMP!
ARGH!
GRR! GET IN THE CAR.
MINX IN CAR

So—
THIS CAR NEEDS AN ORNAMENT.
YOU'LL DO, CHESTER!
TUM-TI-TUM!
BUBBLEGUM
EH?
STICK!

MUTTER! PESKY MINX!
HAW-HAW!
Soon—
CAT'S CRADLE CATTERY
TIME TO DROP YOU OFF, CHESTER OLD FRIEND.
TAKE THAT HORRIBLE LITTLE BEAST AWAY!
DON'T YOU LIKE CHESTER?
NOT HIM — HER!
CAT'S C LE

So—
GOODBYE. SOB!
RASP!
later—
I FEEL GUILTY ABOUT POOR OLD CHESTER — I HOPE HE'LL FORGIVE ME.
ZZZ
SLUDGELY-ON-SEA
MILK
HOT COLD
DON'T WORRY, READERS — I WILL. CHUCKLE!
MORE FISH, ANYONE?

The BEANO BIRDS
MILK
SLURP! I FANCY SOME MILK.
So—
NOW TO REMOVE THE BOTTLE TOP.
SWOOP!
DODGE BOOK
PECK!
EASY!
HOVER!
SLURP! WONDER IF I CAN REACH A LITTLE MORE?
SLOOP!
But—
TOPPLE!
WOOPS!
WRIGGLE!
HELP! BURBLE HELP!
WOBBLE!
TOPPLE!
YAHOO! I'VE FOUND A WAY TO GET ALL THE MILK. SLURP!
GUZZLE!

DANNY'S NANNY
GROAN! DANNY'S GOT A NEW BOUNCER!
GIBBER!
HOI!
STILL, HE'LL GET FED UP WITH IT SOON.
Soon —
I'M FED UP WITH THIS!
WHEW! AS I HOPED!
At home —
HEH-HEH! I'LL FILL IT UP WITH ELDERLY CUSTARD!

So—
AARGH!
OOO!
GLUB!
WAHEY!
HELP!
YIPE!
AARGH!
HOI! HERBIE!
SPRING
WINTER
YAWN! TIME TO GET UP. THANKS, NANNY!

SSSSSSSS
EH?
UNLUCKY, MATE!
WAAAH! DOOF!
OOO! I'M OFF TO BED!
THANK GOODNESS THAT'S OVER!
But—
SNORE!
AARGH! NO! HE'S SLEEP-BOUNCING!

THE BASH STREET BUGS
WE'RE THE BASH STREET BUGS!
WE'RE FED UP BEING CATERPILLARS, THOUGH . . .
FALL
TIMBER!
CHOMP! GUZZLE! BURP!
. . . WE NEVER GET ANY GRUB!
TIME FOR A CHANGE — GET KNITTING, TOOTS!
ROLL

SHAN'T BE LONG!
CLICK!
CLICK!
CLICK!
Soon —
SNORT!
SMIFFY ALWAYS GETS IT WRONG!
CLICK! CLICK!
SNORE!
GRUB!
LOTS OF LOVELY COCOONS.
Much later —
WAHEY! WE'VE TURNED INTO BEAUTIFUL MOTHS!
FLAP!
MMM . . .
FLAP!
FLAP!
I'M STARVING!
FLAP!
FLAP!
FLAP!
WELL MOST OF US ARE BEAUTIFUL!
HAR-HAR!
YAWN!
R-I-P!
R-I-P!

HOI!
BUMP!
LET'S GO, PALS!
FLAP!
FLAP!
ZOOM!
PHEW!
WAIT FOR ME — I CAN'T TAKE OFF!
FLAP! FLAP!
FLAP!
FLAP!
FLAP!
BAH!
YEEEOW!
THROB!
THROB!
HAR-HAR! YOU CAN NOW!
PRANG!
So—
SPLAT!
FLAP!
FLAP!
FLAP!
FLAP!
FLAP!
ZOOM!
THIS IS AN INTERESTING PLACE!
CLASS II B WINDOW

WOW! THESE BUGS LOOK JUST LIKE US!
GOOD LOOKING BUG!
AHA!
SCREECH TO A HALT!
I'M NOT HAVING INSECTS IN MY CLASS — THEY'VE GOT TO GO!
SWISH!
COME HERE, PESTS!
SWISH!
SWISH!
Then —
FLAP!
FLAP!
OVER HERE, PALS!
TOPPLE!
BAH! MISSED THEM!

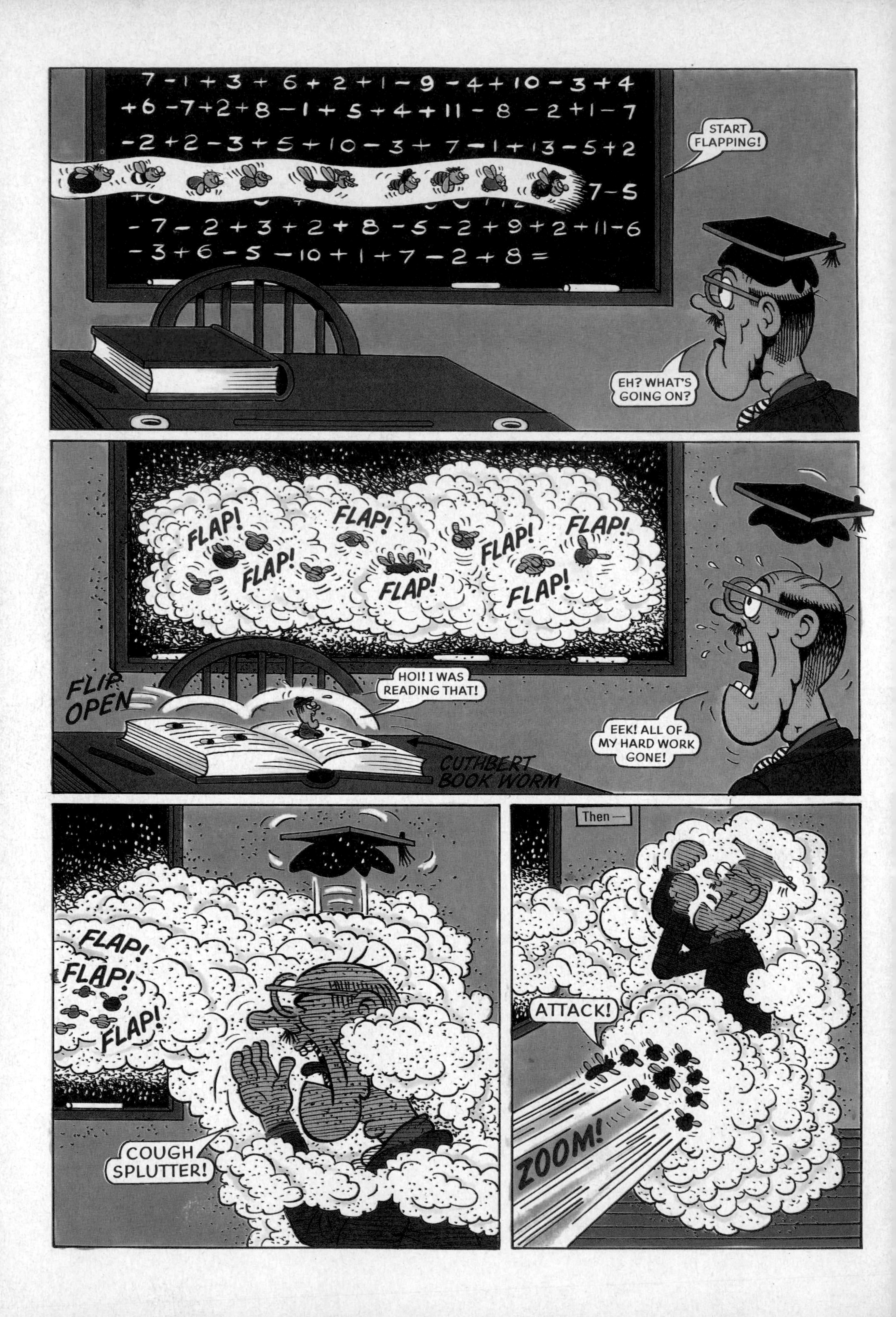

7-1+3+6+2+1-9-4+10-3+4
+6-7+2+8-1+5+4+11-8-2+1-7
-2+2-3+5+10-3+7-1+13-5+2
7-5
-7-2+3+2+8-5-2+9+2+11-6
-3+6-5-10+1+7-2+8=
START FLAPPING!
EH? WHAT'S GOING ON?
FLAP!
FLAP!
FLAP!
FLAP!
FLAP!
FLAP!
FLAP!
FLIP OPEN
HOI! I WAS READING THAT!
CUTHBERT BOOK WORM
EEK! ALL OF MY HARD WORK GONE!
FLAP!
FLAP!
FLAP!
COUGH SPLUTTER!
Then —
ATTACK!
ZOOM!

CHOMP!
MUNCH!
WAH!
BOYLK!
EH?
ZOOM!
HMMM!
SHRIEK!
WAH! HOW EMBARRASSING!
CLASS IIB
ZOOM
YAHOO!
CHUCKLE! WELL DONE, BUGS! YOU GOT RID OF OUR HOMEWORK AND OUR TEACHER AT THE SAME TIME!
HEH-HEH!
WAHEY!

"WHOSE LINE IS IT ANYWAY?"
SOME BEANO CHARACTERS HAVE UNUSUAL USES FOR THEIR CLOTHESLINES!
GREAT PLACE FOR OUR PETS TO SLEEP.
WEEE! I'M A CABLE CAR.
GOOD SHOOTING PRACTICE THIS!

DID I GET SOMETHING WRONG, AGAIN?
SUDSO
TOPPLE!
WOODWORM IN THE POLE. BAD LUCK, JAMES.
PYOING!
OOF!
CHUCKLE! A GREAT CATAPULT THIS!

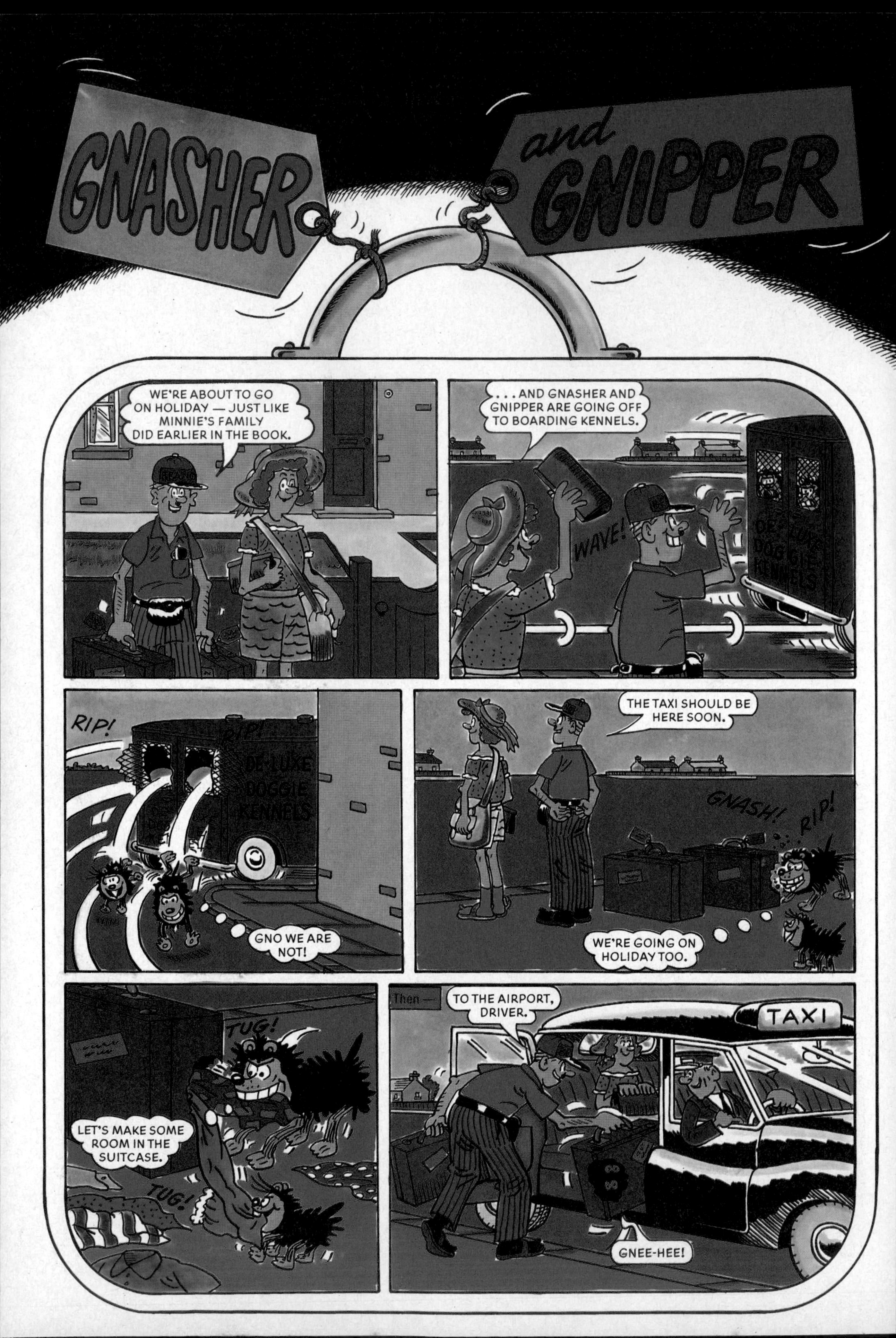
GNASHER
and GNIPPER
WE'RE ABOUT TO GO ON HOLIDAY — JUST LIKE MINNIE'S FAMILY DID EARLIER IN THE BOOK.
. . . AND GNASHER AND GNIPPER ARE GOING OFF TO BOARDING KENNELS.
WAVE!
DE-LUXE DOGGIE KENNELS
RIP!
RIP!
DE-LUXE DOGGIE KENNELS
GNO WE ARE NOT!
THE TAXI SHOULD BE HERE SOON.
GNASH!
RIP!
WE'RE GOING ON HOLIDAY TOO.
TUG!
LET'S MAKE SOME ROOM IN THE SUITCASE.
TUG!
Then —
TO THE AIRPORT, DRIVER.
TAXI
GNEE-HEE!

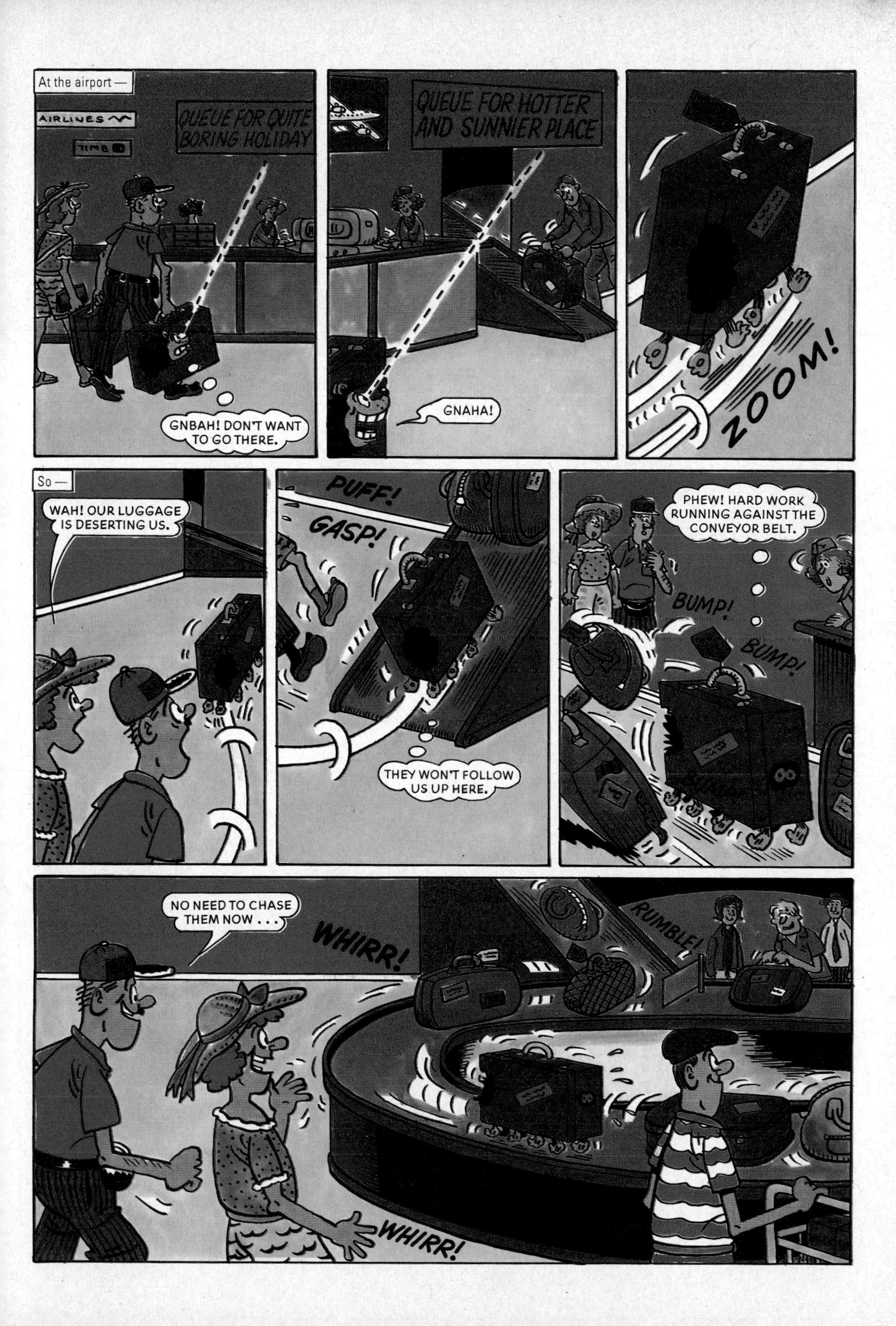
At the airport —
AIRLINES
TIME
QUEUE FOR QUITE BORING HOLIDAY
GNBAH! DON'T WANT TO GO THERE.
QUEUE FOR HOTTER AND SUNNIER PLACE
GNAHA!
ZOOM!
So —
WAH! OUR LUGGAGE IS DESERTING US.
PUFF!
GASP!
THEY WON'T FOLLOW US UP HERE.
PHEW! HARD WORK RUNNING AGAINST THE CONVEYOR BELT.
BUMP!
BUMP!
NO NEED TO CHASE THEM NOW . . .
WHIRR!
RUMBLE!
WHIRR!

. . . THEY'VE TIRED THEMSELVES OUT.
SNORE!
NOW WE CAN GET ON WITH OUR HOLIDAY.
GRAB!
But —
BAH! ALL THAT RUNNING ABOUT HAS MADE US MISS OUR PLANE.
CLOSED FOR TODAY
AIRPORT EXIT
NEVER MIND — THERE IS SOMEWHERE ELSE BOOKED.
GATE 4
SNORE
GRUNT
TAXI
Later —
DE-LUXE DOGGIE KENNELS
PITY ABOUT GNASHER AND GNIPPER, THOUGH.
GNZZZ!
SUCK!
FREEZER (BEST STEAK)
CHOC DROPS
DOG
TAN OIL
AFTER TAN
ICE CREAM
COOL BOX

THE GERMS
ALSO STARRING ILL WILL
GREAT! THERE'S LOTS OF SNOW!
Meanwhile inside Ill Will —
NOT INSIDE WILL THERE ISN'T!
BUT WE'LL SOON SORT THAT.
TO WILL'S FEET

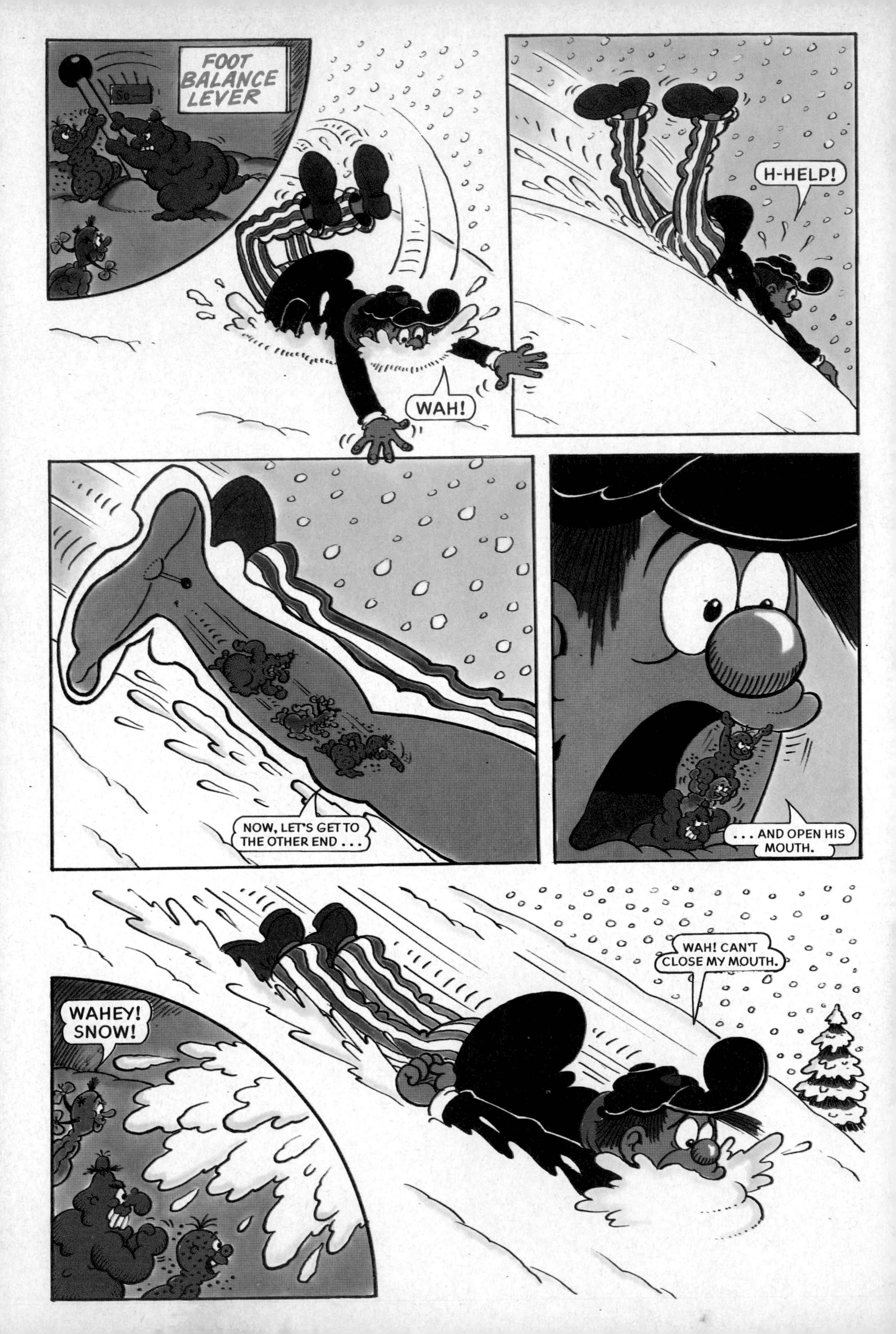
FOOT BALANCE LEVER
WAH!
H-HELP!
NOW, LET'S GET TO THE OTHER END . . .
. . . AND OPEN HIS MOUTH.
WAH! CAN'T CLOSE MY MOUTH.
WAHEY! SNOW!

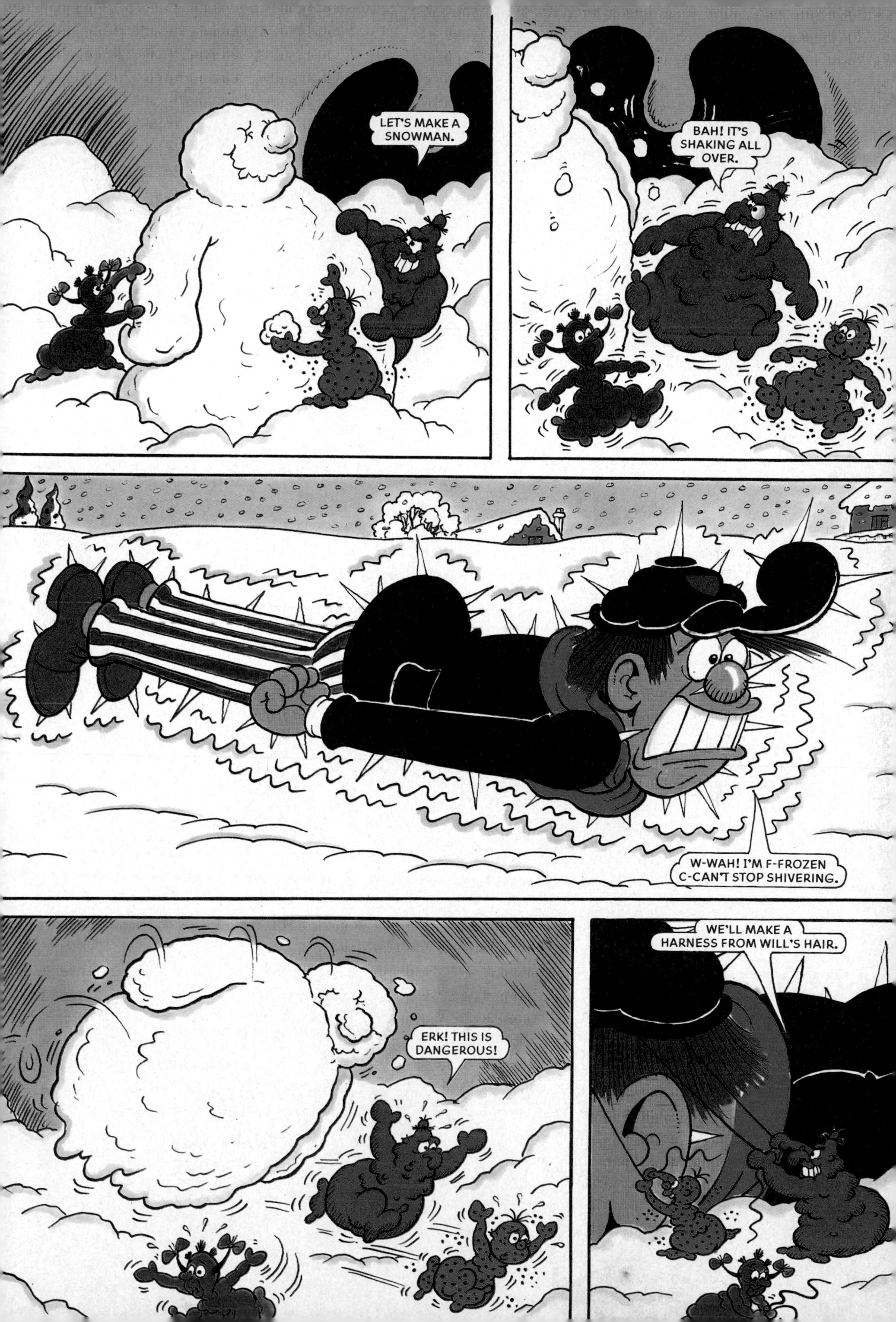
LET'S MAKE A SNOWMAN.
BAH! IT'S SHAKING ALL OVER.
W-WAH! I'M F-FROZEN C-CAN'T STOP SHIVERING.
ERK! THIS IS DANGEROUS!
WE'LL MAKE A HARNESS FROM WILL'S HAIR.

AND PULL HIM OFF
TO SOMEWHERE WARMER.
THIS SAUNA WILL DO.
GREAT! ALL THIS
STEAM HAS THAWED
ME OUT.
AND IT WILL ALSO STOP
US BEING PUNISHED FOR
WHAT WE DID.
WHERE ARE THOSE PESKY GERMS?
CAN'T FIND THEM!
HEE-HEE!
Aunty Biotic —
the Germs'
bossy relative.

TOOTHY TALES
WALKIES PLEASE, DAD.
TOO DARK, GNASHER.
DAD'S WIRE BRUSH SHOULD HELP.
DAD'S TOOL BOX
SQUEEZE
GIANT TOOTH-PASTE
SCRUB
Presently —
YOUR TEETH ARE BETTER THAN ANY TORCH.

NUMBER
13

WELCOME TO THE HALLOWE'EN PARTY!
LET'S DUCK FOR BLOOD ORANGES!
SLURP!
OH-OH!
SORRY, WOLFIE. I LOST MY HEAD!
ANOTHER GAME. WHO CAN GRAB THE TREACLE SCONES!
HEH-HEH! I'LL CUT THROUGH THE STRINGS!
OH, NO YOU WON'T!

HOCUS POKUS BING BANG BONG, WATCH HIS PLAN GO BADLY WRONG . . .
SPIN!
GLUB!
HA! HA! HARD LUCK, GRIM REAPER!
Later
THANKS FOR THE GREAT PARTY.
ARE YOU SURE YOU'LL GET HOME ALL RIGHT?
SURE! WE'VE GOT OUR HALLOWE'EN LANTERNS!
HA-HA!
HO! HO!
13
13

I'M OFF TO THE BEACH TODAY!
BAH! A BIG QUEUE FOR THE BUS — I NEED AN "ALL FOURS" DODGE.
BUS STOP
ROGER the DODGER
So —
OOPS — I'VE DROPPED MY FARE!
CHING!
And —
MUST GET IT!
PING!
CHING!

GOT IT!
GRAB!
BUS STOP
ONE PLEASE!
GRUMBLE!
PESKY DODGER!
Inside hut —
I'LL NEED THIS.
ANOTHER GREAT "ALL FOURS" DODGE.
NOT ONLY HAS THIS BEEN A GREAT DISGUISE . . .
. . . IT MAKES A GREAT BEACH TOWEL AS WELL!
FIZZY POP
PING!

Shortly, at the beach —
BAH! TOO CROWDED. NO SPACE FOR ME!
BUS STOP
I'VE GOT A DODGE, THOUGH.
CHANGING HUT
GRRWL!
WAH! AN ESCAPED LION!
CHUCKLE! I'VE CLEARED THE BEACH!
RUN FOR YOUR LIVES!
BAH! IT WAS ONLY THE DODGER!
WOW!
Then —
YOU LITTLE PEST! MY DONKEY STAMPEDED WHEN HE SAW THE "LION"!
ULP!

DONKEY RIDES
SOB!
LOOK AT ALL THESE DISAPPOINTED CHILDREN!
BOO-HOO!
So —
I'M BACK ON ALL FOURS NOW, READERS . . .
. . . UNFORTUNATELY THIS ISN'T A DODGE. GROAN!
DON'T WORRY, ROGER. ONLY ANOTHER FIFTY RIDES TO GO!
CHUCKLE! GREAT TO HAVE A DAY OFF!
DODGER RIDES
GASP!
PANT!
WHEEZE!
RN

WHAT'S COOKING?
With the BEANO bakers!

WILL THE BISCUITS YOU'RE GOING TO BAKE HAVE ICING ON THEM, MUM?
ER . . . NO! I DON'T HAVE ANY ICING SUGAR LEFT!
Bon Appetit
LET'S GO OUT TO THE SHOPS AND BUY SOME!
BEANO
WAHEY!
WE ALL LIKE BAKING BISCUITS!
BEANO
CHORTLE!
Homepride
Flour
WE'LL NEED SOME FLOUR!

So—
NNNGH! I CAN'T REACH TO OPEN THE BAG!
Then—
Much mixing later—
WE'LL HAVE TO ROLL OUT THE MIXTURE NOW!
IT'S PRETTY FLAT — EXCEPT FOR THAT BIT!

WHERE HAS EVERYONE GONE?
CHORTLE! I COULDN'T STOP!
A SPOT OF LOG ROLLING FOR US!
PLUG! HOW'D YOU GET UNDER THERE?
I KNOW! WE'LL MAKE PLUG- SHAPED BISCUITS!
DOH!

Shortly—
THAT'S IT— PUT THE BISCUITS ON THE BAKING TRAY!
Much later—
WHAT'S BEEN GOING ON HERE?
I'VE NO IDEA, MUM!
PLUG-SHAPED BISCUITS! BUT HOW . . . ?
DO YOU KNOW, READERS?
SSSSH!

Go, Granny, Go!
PARK
LOOK AT THESE DOZY OLD DUFFERS!
GIMME THAT — I'LL LIVEN YOU UP.
OH, WHEN THE SAINTS GO MARCHING IN...
ER — WOULD YOU LIKE A SWEET?
YES . . .

SNATCH!
. . . BUT NOT ONE, — THE WHOLE LOT!
PHWHURRPPP!
THEN I CAN SHARE THEM WITH DENNIS AND HIS PALS.
Then —
KNITTING IS FAR TOO BORING FOR ME.
CLICKETTY CLICKETTY CLICK.
SO EMBARRASSED
Brian Walker

FOOTBALL IS MORE LIKE MY STYLE!
CLICK! CLICK!
WHOP!
HEH-HEH!
Then —
YOU'LL NEED THIS, GRAN.
KNEW IT! SHE'S TIRED HERSELF OUT.
ZOOOOOOMM!
MY GRAN EXHAUSTED? BE SERIOUS!
SKATEBOARD PARK

YOU MUST
I'M GREAT AT ANIMAL IMPRESSIONS! I bit the postman yesterday!
HARRIET GAUDEN CANTERBURY
LAWRENCE WILSON GLASGOW
WHAT'S BLACK AND WHITE AND EATS LIKE A HORSE? A Zebra!
STEVEN ASH BIRMINGHAM
BEANO
WHAT DO YOU CALL A RICH BEAR? Winnie the Pools!
TRACEY CARROLL YORKSHIRE
HOW DO YOU STOP A SKUNK FROM SMELLING? Hold it's nose!

BE JOKING!
KAREN BAKER
COLCHESTER
WHAT CAN FLY UNDERWATER? A bee in a submarine!
WHAT'S BLACK AND WHITE AND FOUND IN AFRICA? A penguin on holiday!
ALICE BIGGINS
NORMANDY
WHAT DO YOU GET WHEN YOU CROSS A FOOTBALL PLAYER WITH A SMOKED FISH? A goalkipper!
DEBBORAH MOGERE
LONDON
ALL PHOTO SENDERS WIN A SELECTION OF BEANO GOODIES!

LiTTLE
I'M GOING TO TELL YOU HOW MEMBERS OF UM TRIBE GOT THEIR INTERESTING NAMES.
THAT'S DANCES WITH WOLVES — HE COULDN'T GET UM PARTNER FOR UM FORMATION RAIN DANCE.
QUICK STEP
NEXT, WRESTLES UM BEARS.
PLUCK
PRAIRIE BLOSSOM CONJURES UP UM PICTURE OF UM BEAUTIFUL YOUNG SQUAW . . .
IN FACT SHE'S MORE LIKE UM WARTY OLD CACTUS!
CHEEKY YOUNG BRAVE!
ZOOM

PLUM
KILL! KILL!
HE LOVES PLAYING WITH HIS TEDDIES.
WRESTLE
THIS IS DARK CLOUD HE ALWAYS BURNS UM TOAST!
ANY GUESSES WHO THIS IS? THAT'S RIGHT — RUNNING NOSE.
SNIFF
HOW DID YOU GET YOUR NAME?
READER'S VOICE
ACTUALLY, LITTLE PLUM ISN'T MY FULL NAME . . .
PLUCK
. . . IT'S REALLY LITTLE PLUM STEALING VARMINT!
FUME
CHIEF'S PLUM TREE

At a secret location — somewhere in Britain.
DO YOU THINK WE'LL EVER MAKE CONTACT WITH OTHER BEINGS IN OUTER SPACE?
MUSIC SENDER
Suddenly —
HELLO, EARTH!
CRACKLE
FZZT!
WOW!
WE'LL FETCH SOME WORLD LEADERS TO TALK TO YOU.
DON'T BOTHER . . .
BILLY WHIZZ!
. . . THIS IS THE ONLY EARTHLING I WISH TO MEET!
ZOOM!
FIND BILLY WHIZZ!
BRING HIM HERE — NOW!

Soon, at Billy's house —
SECRET AGENT
DON'T TELL ANYONE
AHA! A COUPLE OF SECRET AGENTS. WHAT DO YOU WANT?
COUGH! COUGH!
SCREECH!
A TOP SECRET MATTER, BILLY. YOU'LL HAVE TO COME ALONG TO OUR TOP SECRET LOCATION.
OKAY!
JOG!
But —
WAA! AGENT 'D' — YOU DON'T HAVE TO WEAR A BLINDFOLD!
WEAVE!
SWERVE!
TWIRL
Soon, at the top secret place —
HELLO, BILLY WHIZZ. I WANT YOU AND YOUR FAMILY TO COME TO MY PLANET — ZORK. A TAXI WILL COLLECT YOU.
CHORTLE!
HUSH-HUSH TOP SECRET RESEARCH INSTITUTE. NO PEEPING.
DON'T BOTHER TAKING ME HOME, AGENTS. I'LL MANAGE BY MYSELF.
ZIP
Later —
TAXI
ER . . . THE PLANET ZORK, PLEASE!
OKAY, MATE!

Seconds later—
PHEW! GLAD I'M NOT PAYING THIS FARE!
£193867667432114
WAA!
FHOOSHT!
WELCOME TO ZORK, BILLY WHIZZ!
THANKS! BUT WHY AM I HERE?

YOU ARE HERE TO REPRESENT EARTH IN AN INTER-PLANET RACE HERE TOMORROW.
SPORTS STADIUM
WOW! A SPACE RACE MEETING!
WE WANT TO DO A BIT OF SHOPPING, BILLY.
I'M OFF FOR A RUN. SEE YOU ALL LATER!
ZOOM!
HA-HA! GREAT PLACE THIS!
NEEK!
NYIKE!
Later —
ZORKSHOP
I'M GOING BACK TO THE HOTEL FOR AN EARLY NIGHT NOW, FAMILY.
Early next morning —
HOTEL
NOTHING LIKE AN EARLY MORNING TRAINING RUN.
MILKO
The Daily Disc.
After breakfast —
SP
READY TO RACE?
YES, MUM.
Soon —
THIS'LL BE QUITE AN EVENT!
VROOM

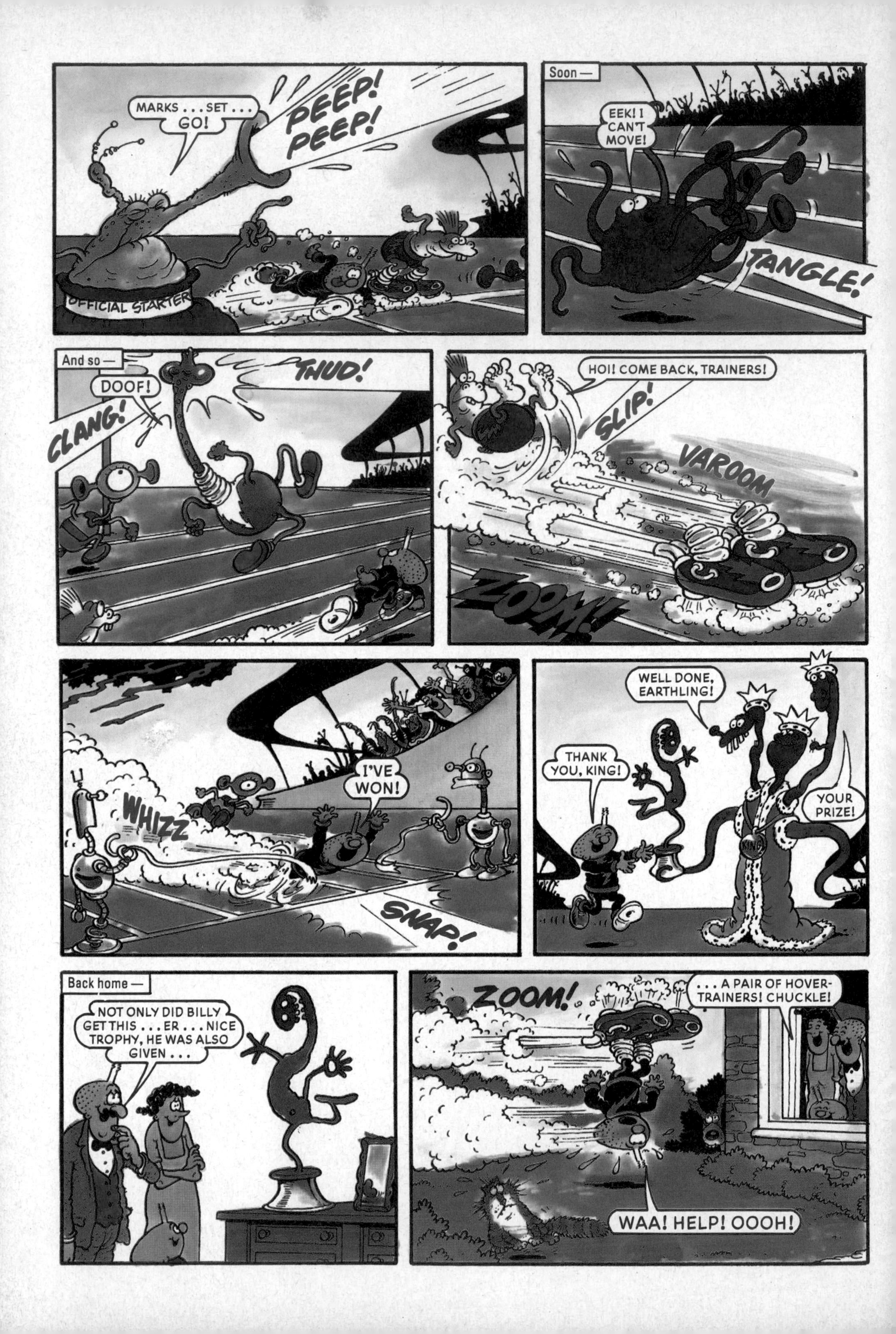
MARKS . . . SET . . . GO!
PEEP! PEEP!
OFFICIAL STARTER
Soon —
EEK! I CAN'T MOVE!
TANGLE!
And so —
DOOF!
CLANG!
THUD!
HOI! COME BACK, TRAINERS!
SLIP!
VAROOM
ZOOM!
WHIZZ
I'VE WON!
SNAP!
WELL DONE, EARTHLING!
THANK YOU, KING!
YOUR PRIZE!
KING
Back home —
NOT ONLY DID BILLY GET THIS . . . ER . . . NICE TROPHY, HE WAS ALSO GIVEN . . .
ZOOM!
. . . A PAIR OF HOVER-TRAINERS! CHUCKLE!
WAA! HELP! OOOH!

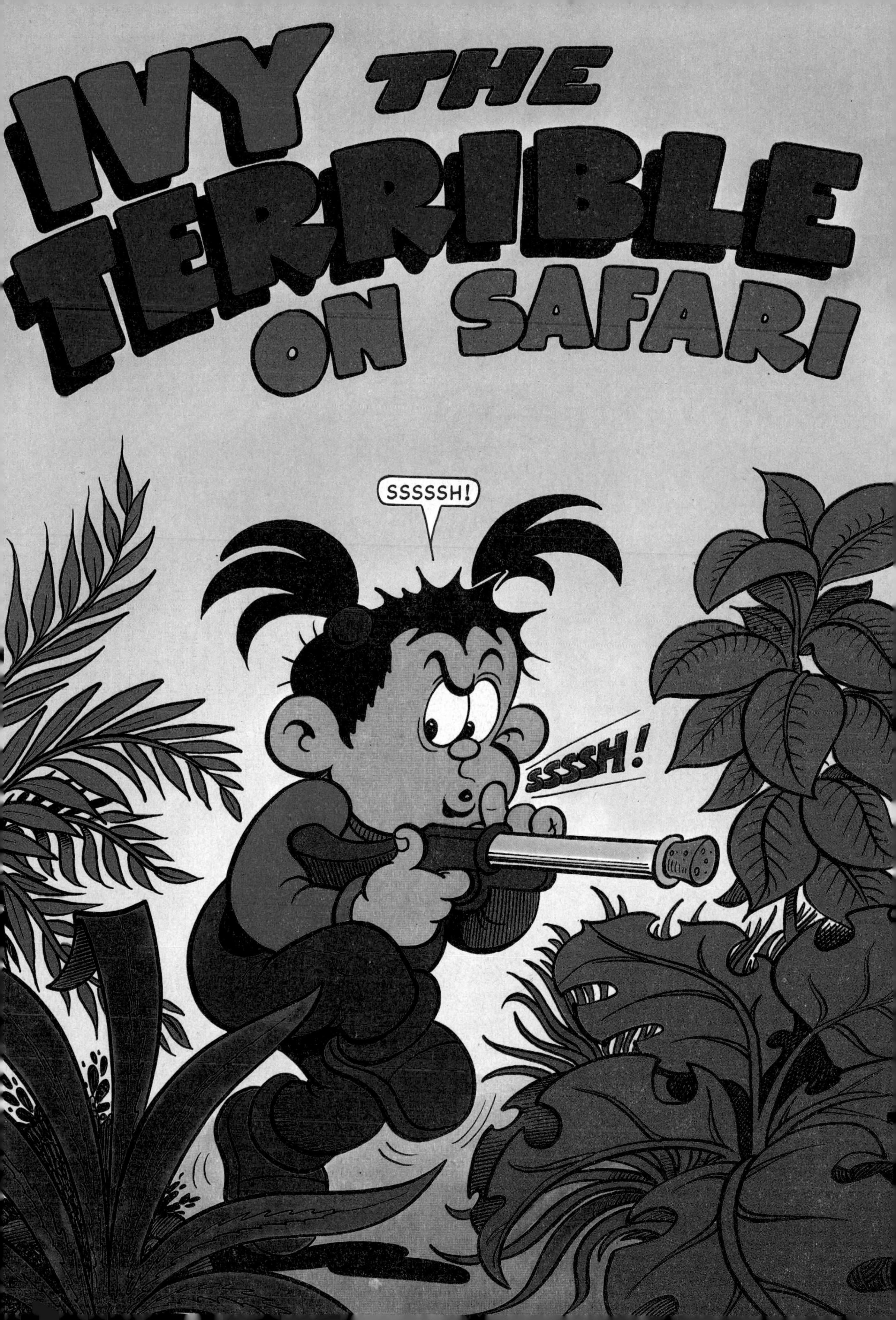
IVY THE TERRIBLE ON SAFARI
SSSSSH!
SSSSH!

I'M AFTER BIG GAME!
Then—
POP!
GOT HIM!
HUH! THE FUN ENDS HERE!
I'M NOT REALLY ON SAFARI. ONLY CRAWLING THROUGH SOME POT PLANTS HUNTING MY SOFT TOYS!

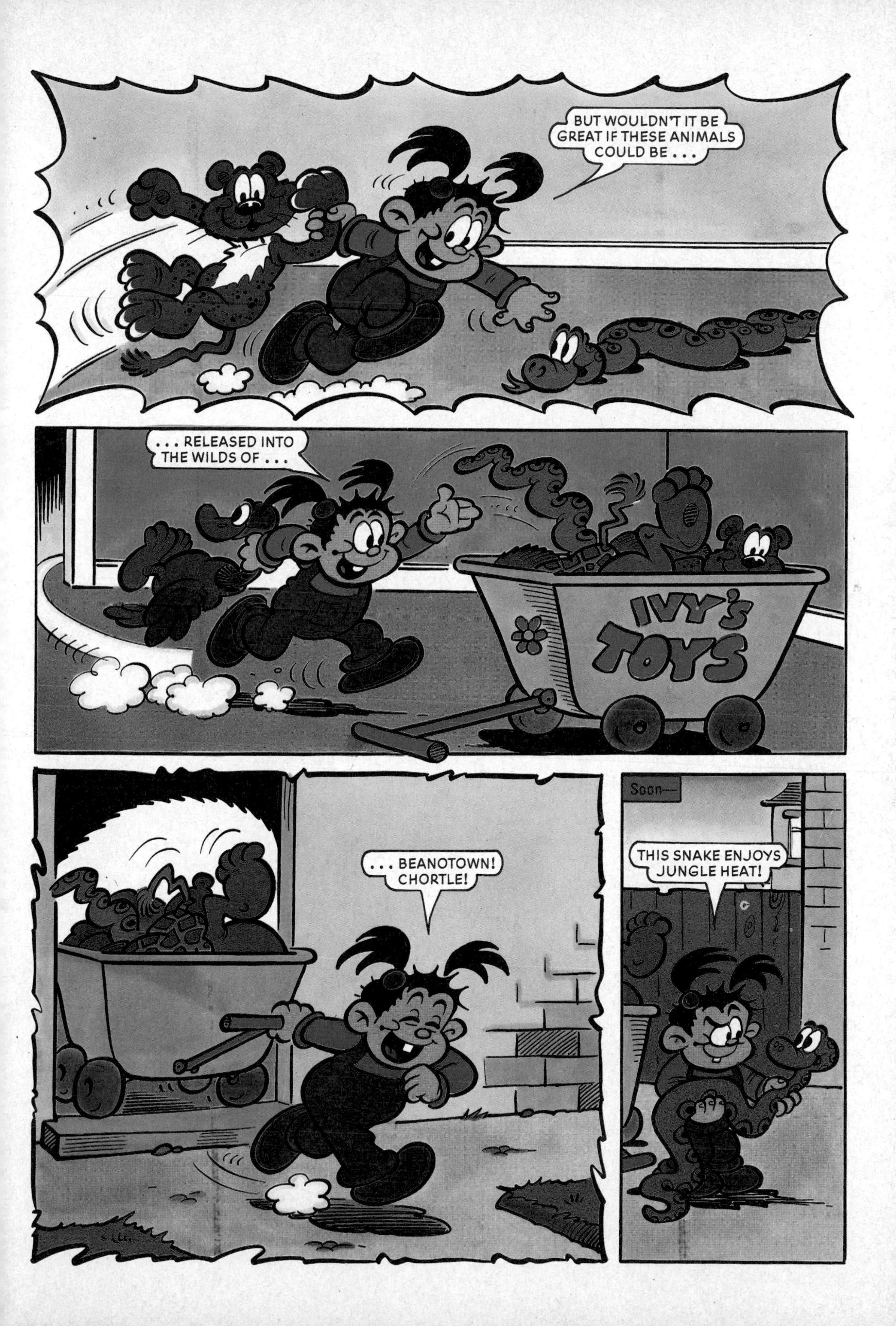
BUT WOULDN'T IT BE GREAT IF THESE ANIMALS COULD BE . . .
. . . RELEASED INTO THE WILDS OF . . .
IVY'S TOYS
. . . BEANOTOWN! CHORTLE!
Soon—
THIS SNAKE ENJOYS JUNGLE HEAT!

So—
PERFECT!
WAH!
A . . . SNAKE!
SCREECH!!
HELP! SCREAM!
BEANOTOWN SAUNA
HO-HO! SAMMY THE SNAKE WILL BE HAPPY IN THERE!
Next—
THIS GIRAFFE'S NOT HAPPY BECAUSE . . .

... HE'S TOO SMALL! HMM!
Soon—
TUM . . . TEE . . . TUM!
Then—
YIKES
A GIRAFFE!
IS THIS YOUR IDEA OF A JOKE?
EH?
I'VE MADE MY GIRAFFE TALLER! HO-HO!

WELL I DIDN'T THINK IT WAS VERY FUNNY!
OW!
GRR!
SPALOOSH!
GLUB!
CHUCKLE!
Next—
I DON'T THINK MY CHEETAH'S FAST ENOUGH TO BE SET FREE!
So—
HMM!

MAYBE THESE WILL HELP CHEETAH!
THERE! READY TO GO FREE?
OFF YOU GO!
WOW! HE'S A FAST MOVER NOW!
HOI!
YAP!
YIKES!
CLANG!
WAA!
More animal antics in a couple of pages.

IVY'S GOOD
BREADSTICKS . . . are good for playing baseball!
WHACK
HOME RUN! CHORTLE!
YIKES!
BABY BISCUITS . . . make good frisbees!
CLONK!
BANG ON TARGET!
BOP!
FISH FINGERS . . . make good Eiffel Towers.
OO . . . ER!
TWANG!

FOOD GUIDE
SPAGHETTI . . . makes a good disguise.
WHERE'S IVY?
I HAVEN'T SEEN HER.
HEH-HEH!
WAA! MY WALL!
CHEESE
PRAWN
SPRING ONIONS . . . make good paint brushes.
CARROTS . . . make good 'Tiddlywinks'.
YAHOO!
FLIP!
PLOP!
TIDDLES
SPLAT!

NOW YOU'LL HAVE TO CATCH FISH TO SURVIVE IN THE WILD!
But—
HUH! YOU'VE NO CLAWS FOR HUNTING!
HO-HO! THERE — THE NEXT BEST THING!
LET'S SEE IF THIS LION CAN HUNT FOR FOOD!

In the park—
YUM! I LOVE SWEETS!
SWEETS
RUSTLE!
EH! WHAT WAS THAT?
ROAR!
YIKES! A LION!
SWEETS
SWEETS
WAH!

A GOOD BIT OF HUNTING, EH? PITY LIONS DON'T EAT SWEETS! HEH-HEH!
SWEETS
Then—
NNNNGH! GORILLAS LIKE TO SIT . . .
. . . PHEW . . . IN TREES!
HE'S OKAY! HE'LL STAY UP THERE FOR AGES!

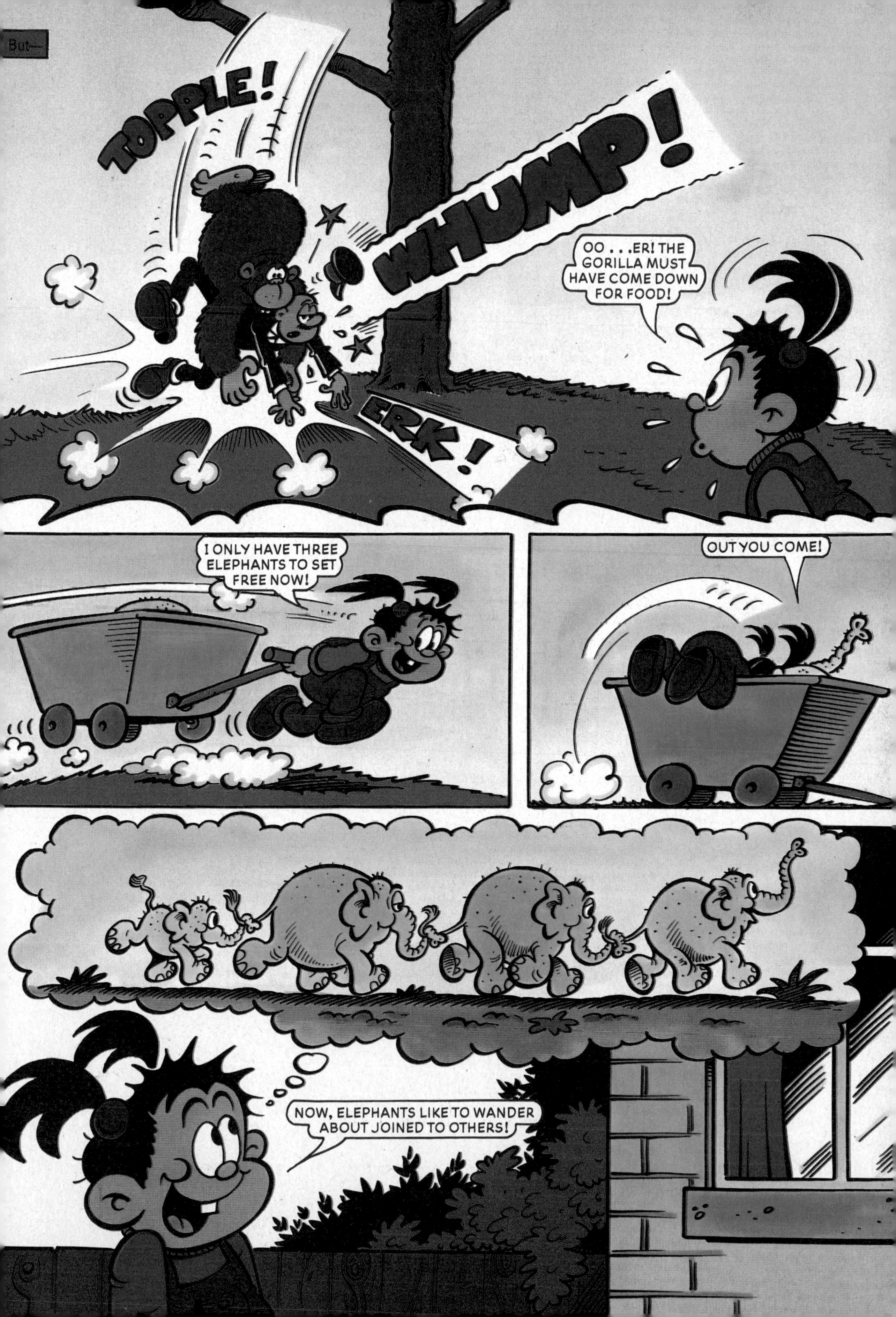

But—
TOPPLE!
WHUMP!
ERK!
OO . . . ER! THE GORILLA MUST HAVE COME DOWN FOR FOOD!
I ONLY HAVE THREE ELEPHANTS TO SET FREE NOW!
OUT YOU COME!
NOW, ELEPHANTS LIKE TO WANDER ABOUT JOINED TO OTHERS!

THAT'S THE WAY I'D BETTER LEAVE THEM!
HA-HA!
CHUCKLE!
HO-HO!
SAFARI OVER — TIME TO GO HOME NOW!
But—
EEK! MAYBE MY ANIMALS WERE REAL AFTER ALL!

GRR! IVY'S BEEN UP TO HER TRICKS IN TOWN!
HUMPH!
PEST!
ULP! THEY'VE ALL 'COME HOME' FOR THE NIGHT! AHEM!
Then—
WAIT A MINUTE, MISTER GORILLA!
ZOOM!
IVY!
ER! HELLO, PARENTS!
Very soon—
WE'VE ALL BEEN SENT TO BED WITHOUT SUPPER! HMM! I WONDER WHAT REAL WILD JUNGLE ANIMALS TAKE TO BED AT NIGHT?

Chortle! Well, we can show you!
ZZZZZ!
SNORE! PURRRRR!
ZZZZ!
HISSSS! ZZZZ!
HA-HA! THEY TAKE 'IVY DOLLS' TO BED!
RN

GENERAL JUMBO
JUMBO JOHNSON is the lucky lad who has his very own armed force of super radio-controlled models.
One summer's day —
DINCHESTER COVE IS JUST THE PLACE TO TEST OUT MY NEW MODEL CARRIER AND SUB.
HEY! GET THAT SHADOW OFF ME — I'M TRYING TO CATCH THE SUN.
HO-HO! YOU'LL BE FRIED TO A CRISP WITH ALL THAT OIL ON, MATHEWS.
Using his special control gadget, Jumbo sent his carrier surging through the waves.
SHE'S LOOKING GOOD!
UGH! WHAT'S THIS STUFF IN THE WATER?
IT LOOKS LIKE AN OIL SLICK.
IT'S HEADING STRAIGHT FOR ME.
I CAN'T GET OUT OF ITS WAY!
F

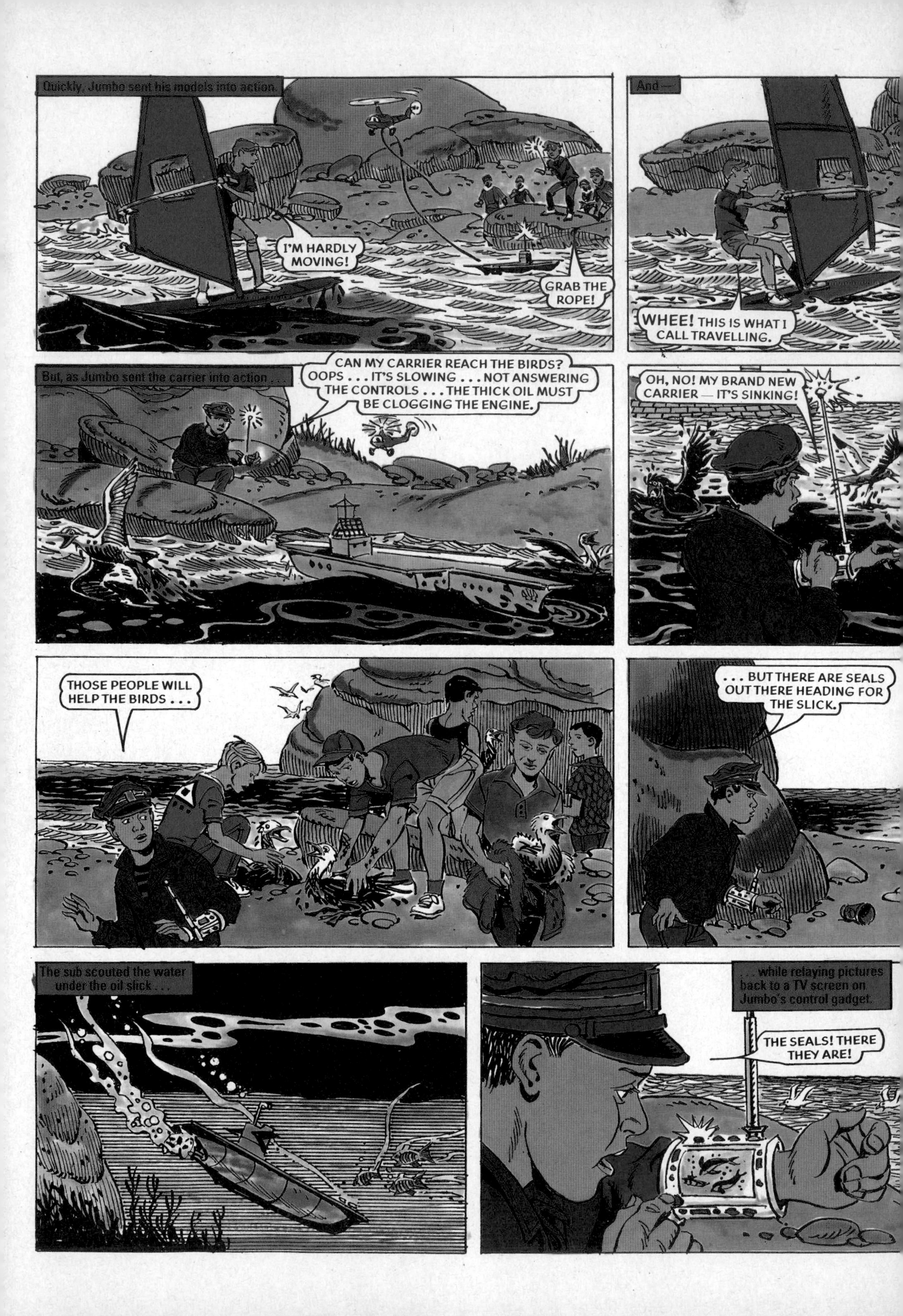
Quickly, Jumbo sent his models into action.
I'M HARDLY MOVING!
GRAB THE ROPE!
And —
WHEE! THIS IS WHAT I CALL TRAVELLING.
But, as Jumbo sent the carrier into action . . .
CAN MY CARRIER REACH THE BIRDS? OOPS . . . IT'S SLOWING . . . NOT ANSWERING THE CONTROLS . . . THE THICK OIL MUST BE CLOGGING THE ENGINE.
OH, NO! MY BRAND NEW CARRIER — IT'S SINKING!
THOSE PEOPLE WILL HELP THE BIRDS . . .
. . . BUT THERE ARE SEALS OUT THERE HEADING FOR THE SLICK.
The sub scouted the water under the oil slick . . .
. . . while relaying pictures back to a TV screen on Jumbo's control gadget.
THE SEALS! THERE THEY ARE!

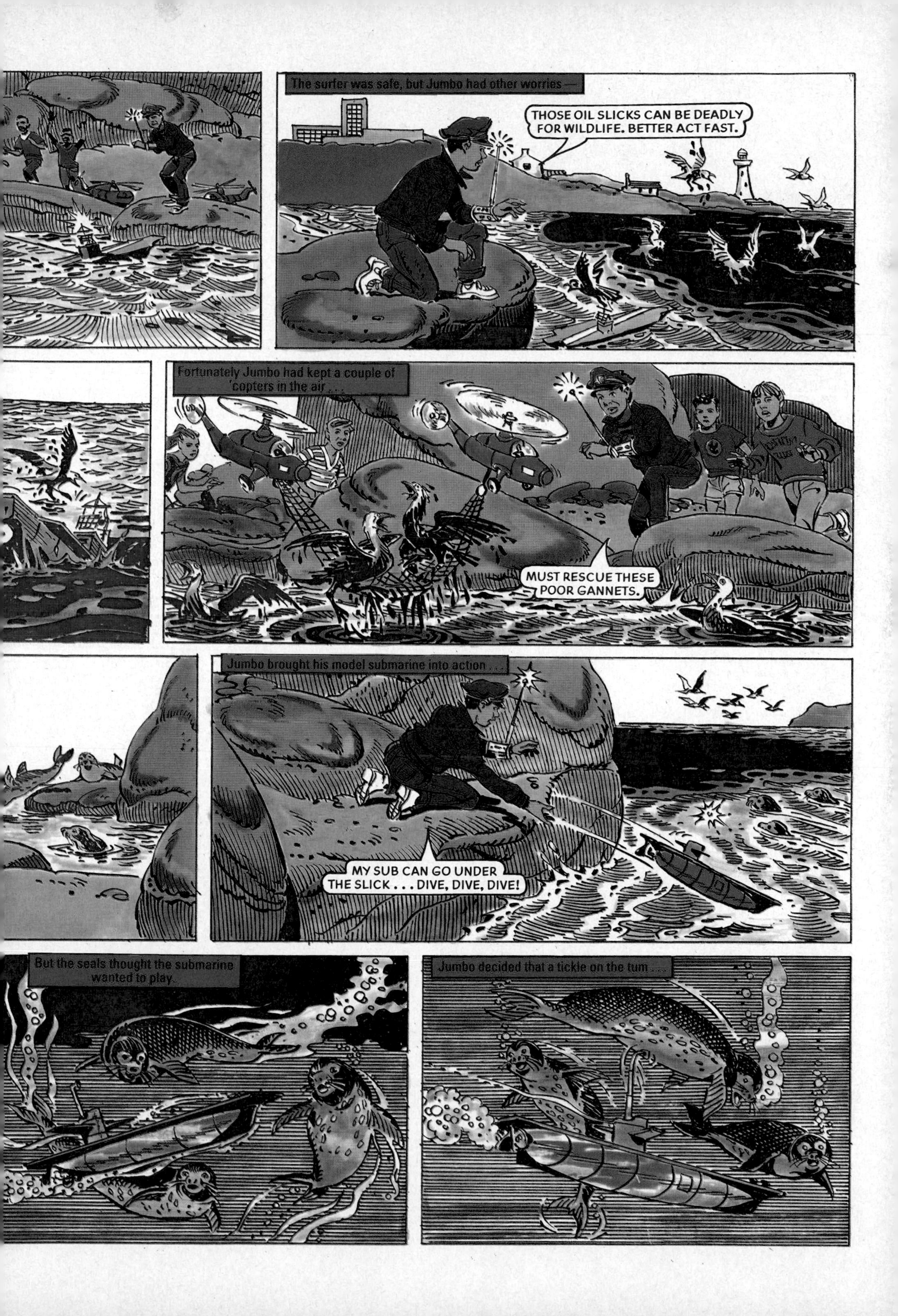
The surfer was safe, but Jumbo had other worries —
THOSE OIL SLICKS CAN BE DEADLY FOR WILDLIFE. BETTER ACT FAST.
Fortunately Jumbo had kept a couple of 'copters in the air . . .
MUST RESCUE THESE POOR GANNETS.
Jumbo brought his model submarine into action . . .
MY SUB CAN GO UNDER THE SLICK . . . DIVE, DIVE, DIVE!
But the seals thought the submarine wanted to play.
Jumbo decided that a tickle on the tum . . .

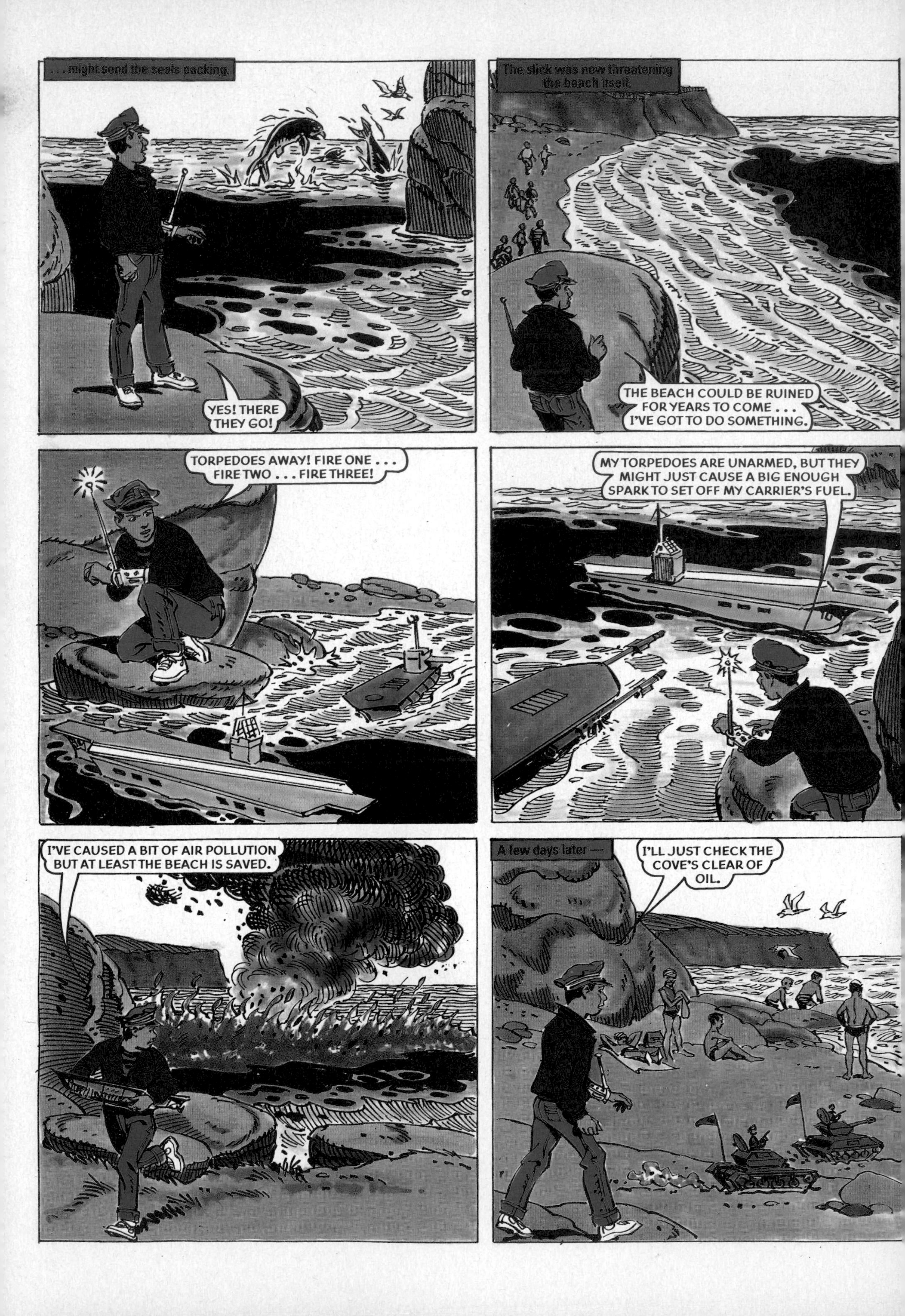

. . . might send the seals packing.
YES! THERE THEY GO!
The slick was now threatening the beach itself.
THE BEACH COULD BE RUINED FOR YEARS TO COME . . . I'VE GOT TO DO SOMETHING.
TORPEDOES AWAY! FIRE ONE . . . FIRE TWO . . . FIRE THREE!
MY TORPEDOES ARE UNARMED, BUT THEY MIGHT JUST CAUSE A BIG ENOUGH SPARK TO SET OFF MY CARRIER'S FUEL.
I'VE CAUSED A BIT OF AIR POLLUTION BUT AT LEAST THE BEACH IS SAVED.
A few days later —
I'LL JUST CHECK THE COVE'S CLEAR OF OIL.

Jumbo sent his submarine on a deeper dive, towards his sunken aircraft carrier.
With great control skills, Jumbo, pushed the carrier to the surface with his submarine.
THERE'S ONLY ONE CHANCE.
SUCCESS! NOW THE CARRIER SHOULD . . .
. . . SET THE OIL SLICK ALIGHT. YE-ES!
A shock was in store —
OIL SLICK!
OH, NO! NOT ANOTHER ONE!
HAW-HAW! IT'S OK, JUMBO. JUST MATHEWS HAVING A DIP!
HO-HO! MATHEWS HAS SO MUCH SUN OIL ON HE MAKES HIS OWN MINI-SLICK!

TOOTHY TALES
HOI! COME BACK!
DENNIS'S VOICE
GNEH?
MY TOYS!
GNAUGHTY BABY-FACE.
ZOOM
DENNIS'S TOY BOX
YUK-YUK!
GNASH!
WALTER'S ABODE
MUST HELP DENNIS.
GRUNCH! GRUNCH! GRUNCH!
PT CHEEEEE!
HAW-HAW! WELL DONE, GNASHER.
PHOO!
SPLAT!
YOW!
ZONK!

DENNIS the MENACE
and GNASHER
WAHEY! IT'S SNOWING!
I'M NEVER COLD IN MY BEDROOM!
MY PET PIG, RASHER BREAKS THE DRAUGHT AT THE FOOT OF THE DOOR! CHORTLE!
SNORE! SNORE! GRUNT!
NNNNGH! ONE PROBLEM — I CAN'T SHIFT HIM!
PUSH
GNNNG!
PSSSST! SWILL TIME!
GRUNT!

GRUNT!
LEAP
YIKES!
CRASH
CHATTER
OO . . . ER! IT'LL BE QUITE A TASK KEEPING THE DRAUGHTS OUT NOW!
SHAKE
ICY BLAST
BREEZE
TREMBLE
In the kitchen.
HURRY UP, GNASHER! WE'RE GOING OUT! CHOMP! CHEW!
EH?
YOU'RE NOT GOING OUT TO PLAY TILL YOU'VE CLEARED THE SNOW OFF THE PATH!
GRAB
AW!
HOLD IT, RASHER! THERE'S A SCRAP OF SWILL LEFT IN HERE!
BOYLP!

HO-HO! HE CAN NEVER LEAVE A DROP!
SLURP!
ZOOM
HA-HA! I KNEW THAT WOULD HAPPEN! THIS WAY, RASHER!
STUCK
HAR-HAR! NO NEED TO DIG THE PATH NOW!
ZOOM
ZOOM
ZOOM
DROP
PUSH
GRUNT! MUST GET THIS OFF MY SNOUT! SNORT!
DON'T SIT DOWN, RASHER. YOU'RE PART OF OUR . . .
Dennis's Shed
. . . 'MENACE BOBSLEIGH TEAM'! HA-HA!
WHOOSH!

WAHEY! WE'RE AT THE START!
START OF BEANO BOBSLEIGH RACE
OINK! PUFF!
HI, CURLY! NICE SLEIGH!
THANKS, DENNIS!
POLISH
STAR
BOB
HO-HO! PIE-FACE IS A 'HOT FAVOURITE'!
BEANO
RACE
READY . . . SET . . .
. . . GO!
PHEEEP!
YAHOO!
PUSH
GRUNT!
WOBBLE
WOBBLE
STUCK
UNRAVEL
HA-HA!
OO . . . MY SLEIGH!
CHORTLE!
HA-HA! FANCY CURLY RUNNERS AREN'T MUCH GOOD FOR GOING DOWNHILL IN A STRAIGHT LINE!
WAA! I'VE LOST CONTROL!
SPIN
WOBBLE
WAHEY! WE'RE GOING TO WIN, GNASHER!
ZOO

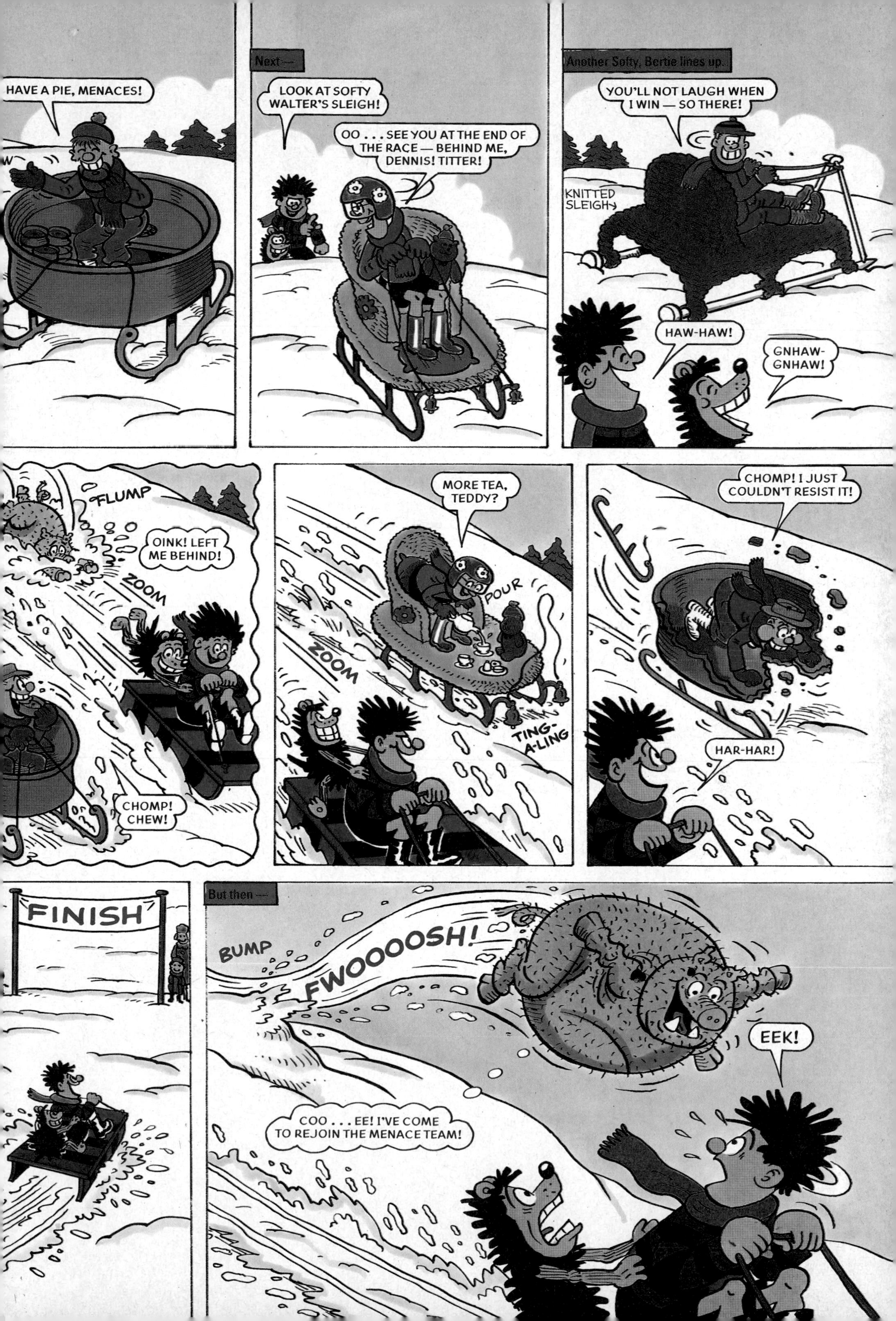
HAVE A PIE, MENACES!
Next —
LOOK AT SOFTY WALTER'S SLEIGH!
OO . . . SEE YOU AT THE END OF THE RACE — BEHIND ME, DENNIS! TITTER!
Another Softy, Bertie lines up.
YOU'LL NOT LAUGH WHEN I WIN — SO THERE!
KNITTED SLEIGH
HAW-HAW!
GNHAW-GNHAW!
FLUMP
OINK! LEFT ME BEHIND!
ZOOM
CHOMP! CHEW!
MORE TEA, TEDDY?
POUR
ZOOM
TING-A-LING
CHOMP! I JUST COULDN'T RESIST IT!
HAR-HAR!
FINISH
But then —
BUMP
FWOOOOSH!
EEK!
COO . . . EE! I'VE COME TO REJOIN THE MENACE TEAM!

SPLAT
GNEEK!
CRUMP
AAAGH!
FINIS
WELL DONE, WALTER!
FINISH
CHEER
I'VE WON!
TING A-LING!
GENTLE SLIDE
OINKWAH!
GRUNT! I'M STILL PUSHING!
GRUNT! PUFF! OINK!
GRRR! JUST WAIT TILL WE'RE FULLY DEFROSTED, RASHER!
GNASH!
HEH-HEH!
PUSH
1ST PRIZE

LES'S PRETEND
LES'S ROOM
EH? WHAT'S THIS DAFT THING ON LES'S DOOR.
SILLY MAN! WE BEES DON'T HAVE DOORS ON OUR HIVES.
I'M OFF TO HOVER ROUND PLANTS AND MAKE HONEY.
But—
CRASH!

HMMM! I'LL HAVE TO GET MY HONEY SOMEWHERE ELSE!
HANDY THINGS SUPERMARKETS! I'LL TAKE THIS HOME AND MAKE IT INTO A HONEYCOMB.
SUP
CHECK-OUT
So—
BEELLY WHIZZ
But—
OH-OH! TOO WARM — IT'S MELTED.
WOW! WONDER WHERE ALL THE HONEY WENT?

Here's where—
POSH PEOPLE PRESS
ARE YOU STUCK UP?
PEST! I'LL GET YOU FOR THAT.
HE WON'T . . .
. . . I'LL STING HIM!
YOWL!
SMACK!
MUM! MUM! I'VE BEEN STUNG.
DON'T WORRY — I'LL CUT AN ONION IN HALF . . .
KNOW YOUR ONION

. . . AND RUB IT IN — THAT'S MEANT TO HELP BEE STINGS.
THANKS — NOW I CAN THROW THE ONIONS AT LES.
WEAR THIS IF YOU ARE GOING TO MESS ABOUT WITH BEES.
WAIT A MINUTE, MUM — LES ISN'T A REAL BEE.
I KNOW — BUT THAT'S VERY HANDY FOR NAILING TO THE WALL TO STOP YOU CHASING HIM ABOUT.
BZZ-HEE-HEE!

MERBOY
LOOK! AN OYSTER BED!
So—
GET UP YOU LAZY LOT! WAKEY-WAKEY!
NYAA!
YAWN! PUSH OFF MERBOY.
NYAA!
NYA! HOW ARE YOU GOING TO MAKE ME?
G

PTCHOO
BY FIRING OUR PEARLS AT YOU.
HAR-HAR! JUST WHAT I WANTED.
NOW I CAN PLAY AT MARBLES.
But presently —
YAWN! THIS IS GETTING BORING.
On the surface —
OCEAN QUEEN
BET THE PEOPLE ON THAT LUXURY LINER WOULD LOVE THESE PEARLS.
N
QUEEN
COOEE! LOOK WHAT I'VE GOT!

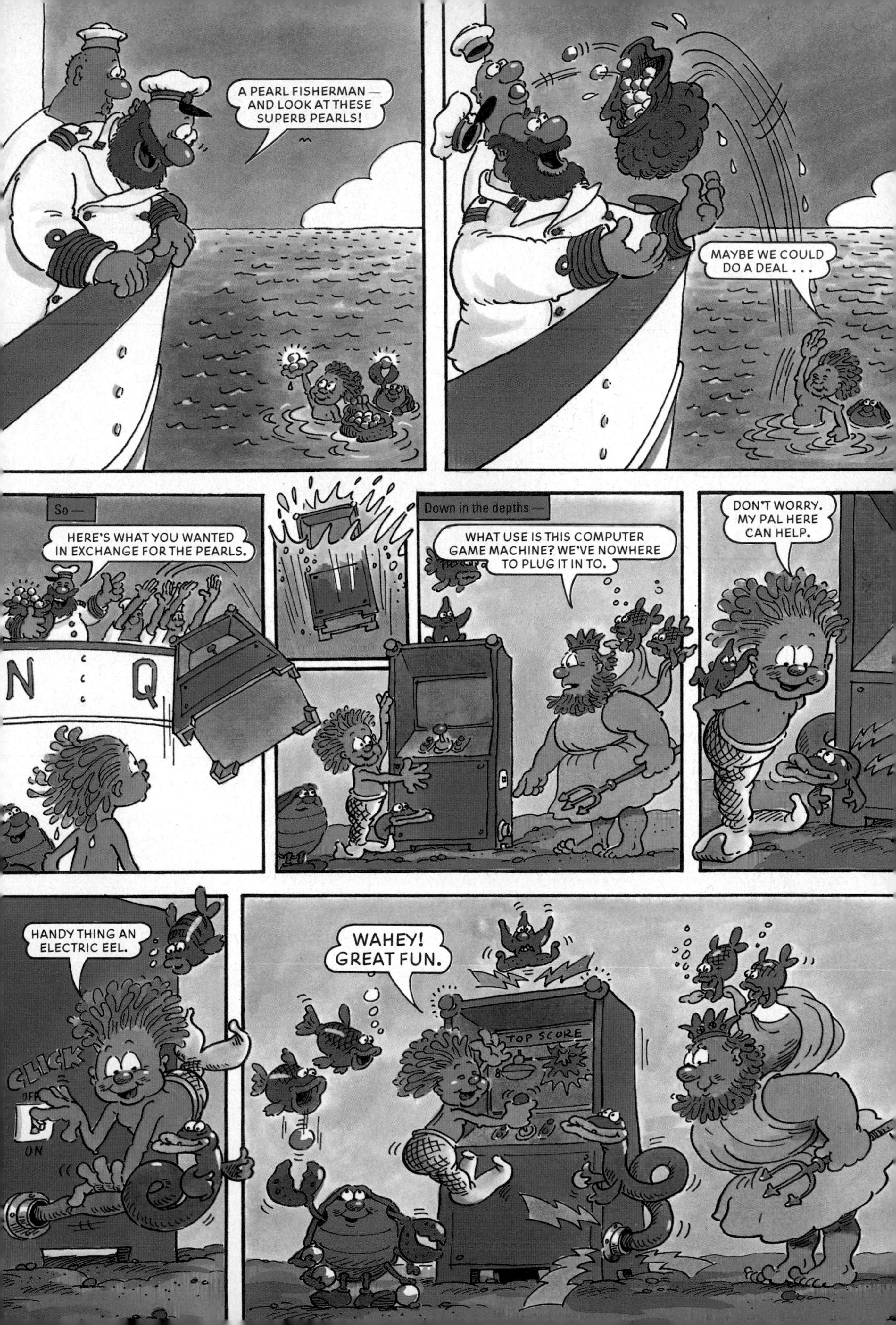
A PEARL FISHERMAN — AND LOOK AT THESE SUPERB PEARLS!
MAYBE WE COULD DO A DEAL . . .
So —
HERE'S WHAT YOU WANTED IN EXCHANGE FOR THE PEARLS.
Down in the depths —
WHAT USE IS THIS COMPUTER GAME MACHINE? WE'VE NOWHERE TO PLUG IT IN TO.
DON'T WORRY. MY PAL HERE CAN HELP.
HANDY THING AN ELECTRIC EEL.
CLICK
ON
WAHEY! GREAT FUN.
TOP SCORE

LITTLE NURSERY

Jack and Jill went up the hill
To fetch a pail of manure —
But I'd set a trap, and Jack, poor old chap,
Soon smelled like he'd bathed in a sewer.

Mary had a little lamb,
It really looked angelic,
Till Larry got some veggie dye
And made it psychadelic.

LARRY'S CRIMES

SHATTER!

SMASH!

Little Jack Horner sat in a corner
Eating a large mushroom quiche —
But I'd filled the bowl with granite and coal.
Said Jack "Thish shtuff's shattered my teesh!"

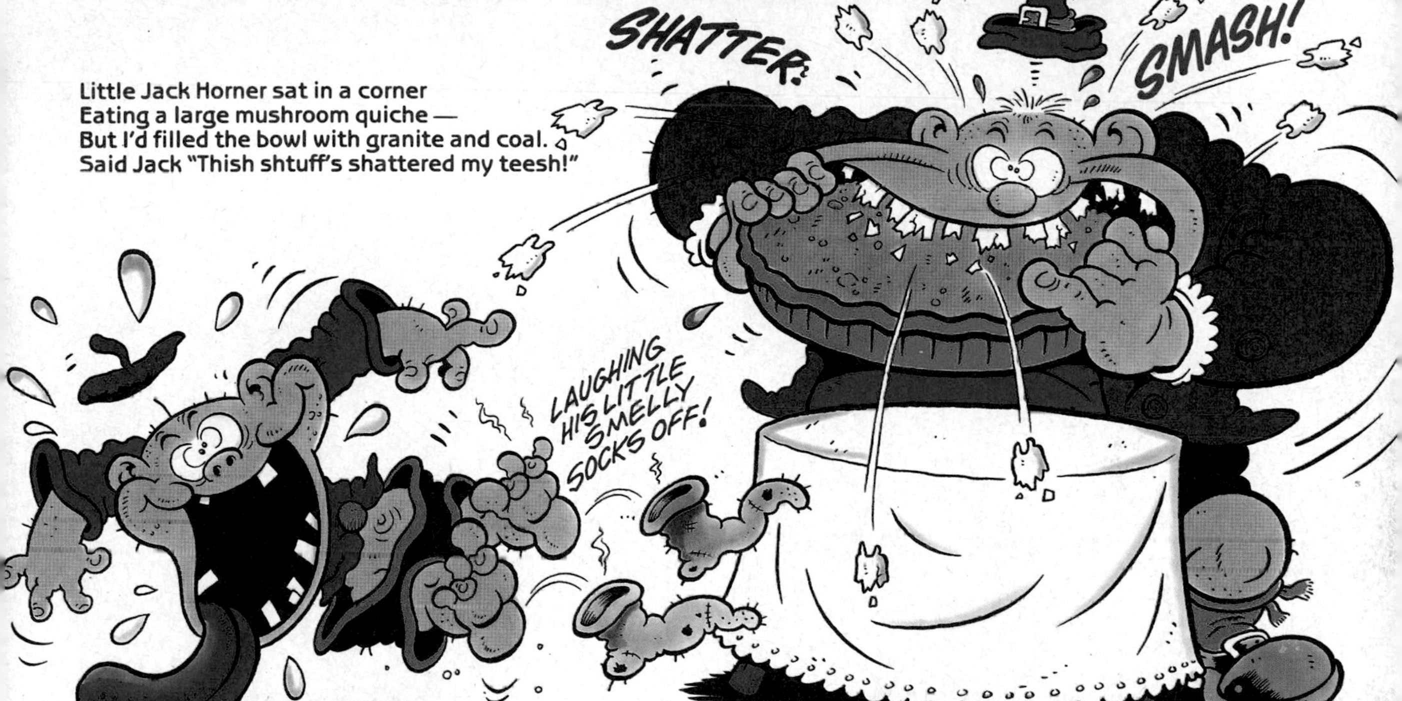

LAUGHING HIS LITTLE SMELLY SOCKS OFF!

AAAAAAGHHH!

Little Miss Muffet sat on her tuffet
Eating spaghetti for tea.
Along came our mate, put worms on her plate,
Then laughed as she screamed, "Tee-hee-hee!"

RAAASPP!

WRIGGLE WIGGLE! WRITHE!

KNICKERS IN A TWIST!

BELCH!

BIFFO
SNAP!
?

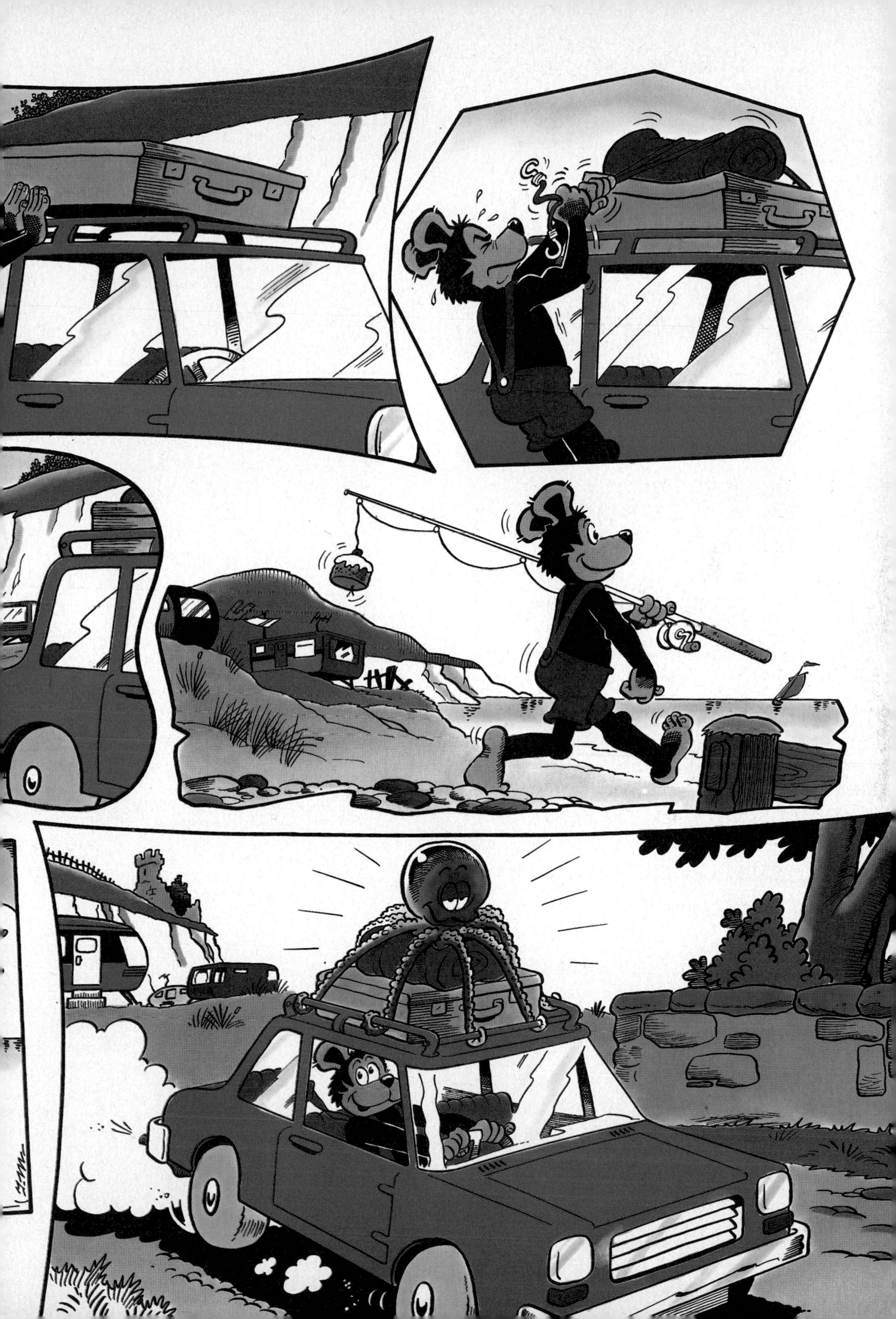

MINNIE the MINX
HMM! I NEED A VICTIM.
AHA! FATTY FUDGE!
So —
TWANG!
But —
DUCK

HOW'D YOU KNOW TO DO THAT?
RASP!
I SAW THE SIGN BACK THERE!
MIN AT WORK
BAH! WHO COULD'VE DONE THIS?
Shortly —
BUS STOP
THIS LOOKS A MORE LIKELY VICTIM.
JUST THE RIGHT ANGLE FOR A NOSTRIL SHOT!

But—
NOT AGAIN! HOW'D YOU KNOW I WAS GOING TO TO THAT?
DODGE
I HEARD A "MIN WARNING" ON THE RADIO!
HUMPH!
DAILY BLAH
BEWARE— MINXING ALL DAY
MUST FIND OUT WHO'S SPOILING MY FUN!
WATCH OUT-MINX ABOUT!
THIS IS GETTING RIDICULOUS!
Then—
DAD — I MIGHT'VE KNOWN!
KEEP SAFE FROM MINXIN
CHORTLE! THIS CAMPAIGN WILL KEEP MIN FROM DOING ANY MINXING!

ERK! MINNIE!
THAT'S WHAT YOU THINK!
KEEP SAFE FROM MINX NG
WAAH!
WRAP!
I HAVEN'T MINXED ANYONE ALL DAY . . .
So—
. . . SO DAD'LL HAVE TO TAKE A FULL DAY'S MINXING ON HIS OWN. CHORTLE!
TICKLE!
SQUIRT
ROLL!
HA-HA! GLUB! OOF! HA-HA! GLUB! OOF!

TOOTHY TALES
EEK!
RIP!
Soon —
RIP!
RIP!
RIP!
ZOOM!
And —
RIP!
At an aerobics class —
RIP!
RIP!
GNEE! GNEE!
Back home —
I'M F-FREEZING!
CHATTER!
THESE BITS OF CLOTH MADE A GREAT QUILT FOR MY LITTLE BOY.
COMFY!

BALL BOY
I'M SUBSTITUTE THIS WEEK — BETTER FIND A PLACE ON THE BENCH.
HMM! LOTS OF PEOPLE ON THE BENCH TODAY. MANAGER, TRAINER, SUBS . . .
. . . SPONSORS, CLUB DOCTOR, CLUB PSYCHIATRIST, BAND FOR HALF-TIME . . .
. . .AT LAST, A SPACE!

Then —
EH? WHY AM I WATCHING HOCKEY.
WOW! THIS BENCH IS SO LONG IT STRETCHES ON TO THE NEXT PITCH.
WOW! ROUGH GAME, HOCKEY.
BRING ON ANOTHER SUB!
ON YOU COME.
B-BUT!
OOOER!

I KNOW!
I'LL BE SAFE UP HERE.
RUMBLE
MAYBE NOT.
USELESS! BUT MAYBE YOU COULD GO IN GOAL.
So—
LOT'S OF PADS TO PUT ON.
SILLY BOY — YOU PUT IT ON BACKWARDS.
I KNOW WHAT I'LL DO . . .

Soon —
THAT'S MORE LIKE IT.
Then —
GREAT SAVE!
And —
WOW! ANOTHER GREAT SAVE.
LET'S CHAIR HIM OFF THE FIELD — THOSE SAVES WON US THE MATCH.

But —
EH?

THE BEST WAY TO PLAY HOCKEY IS TO LEAVE IT TO YOUR PADS! I WAS HERE ALL THE TIME, HA-HA!

BABY-FACE FINLAYSON
SNIFF
MOUTHWATERING AROMA
MY SENSITIVE NOSTRILS DETECT THE AROMA OF GINGERBREAD MEN!
Inside —
I DON'T JUST MAKE GINGERBREAD MEN, I MAKE GINGERBREAD FAMILIES!
GINGERBREAD NIFF
HMM! A THIEF, EH?
GET OUT OF IT!
WHAM!
OO-OO-OO! MY POOR HANDIE!
LEAP
THESE AREN'T FOR THE LIKES OF YOU!
SUCH PAIN!
THROB!

At the park —
THEY'RE FOR MY DUCK PAL!
TOSS!
FORTUNATELY MY FINE MOTORISED PRAM HAS ANOTHER USE . . .
ZOOM!
Soon —
. . . IT CAN ALSO BE A SUBMAPRAM!
PRESS
SPLOSH!
DIVE! DIVE! DIVE!
SHOOOOOM!
TIME TO SURFACE!
THERE YOU ARE, LITTLE DUCK.
AND HERE AM I!

THERE! HAVE THE LOT! ERK!
THROW
OPEN
SHE'S TOO KIND! YUK-YUK!
BUMP!
GRR! THIEF!
SQUAWK!
SUCH A CLEVER LITTLE BANDIT!
Back home —
YOUR SOUP'S OUT, MY LITTLE ONE.
EXCELLENT! I'M STILL HUNGRY, "MUMSIE-FACE"!
BIB
I'VE COOLED DOWN YOUR SOUP IN CASE IT BURNT YOUR LITTLE MOUTH!
TA!
Suddenly —
SOAR!
OO-ER! IT'S THE FEATHERED, QUACKING CREATURE.
YOU PINCHED MY LUNCH, SO I'LL PINCH YOURS!
HMPH! ONLY FAIR, I SUPPOSE!

ROGER the DODGER
MUST BE QUIET!
I NEED A MOUSE FOR A DODGE.
GOT IT!
SQUEAK!

NOW TO ADD THE FINISHING TOUCHES.
THERE — A PERFECT METAL DETECTOR!
NOW FOR STAGE TWO OF MY DODGE.
METAL DETECTOR FOR SALE- £10
THUD!
And—
LET'S SEE IT WORK!
So—
WOW! IT'S SQUEAKING!
OKAY!
SQUEAK! SQUEAK!

THERE'S SOMETHING UNDER HERE!
SQUEAK!
SQUEAK!
WAHEY!
TOLD YOU!
THAT'S GREAT!
CHUCKLE! I BURIED THESE HERE LAST NIGHT!
GREAT THING THIS!
So—
I'LL BUY IT!
TA!
£10
Next day—
THIS THING IS USELESS FOR FINDING MONEY!
SQUEAK!
ULP!

DON'T WORRY — I DON'T WANT MY MONEY BACK . . .
SQUEAK!
. . . I'VE FOUND ANOTHER USE FOR IT.
SQUEAK!
SQUEAK!
IT'S A GREAT CHEESE DETECTOR!
SQUEAK
SLURP!
MY MUM'S ALWAYS HIDING PIZZAS FROM ME!
CHOMP!
CHUCKLE! GLAD TO SEE THE MOUSE HAS FOUND A GOOD HOME!
R.N.

ARE YOU AS DAFT
Answer the questions below to find out. Please hold this page the right way up before you start. Do not attempt while riding a bicycle, tightrope walking or taking part in a knife throwing act or you might hurt yourself.
What do you get hanging from cherry trees?
A) Sore arms.
B) A lost mole.
C) An elephant with his toenails painted red.
What do you put in an Irish Stew?
A) Half a peat bog and a pound of shamrocks.
B) Your teeth.
C) Leprechaun's toenails and Terry Wogan's wig.
What do you get if you cross a collie and a sheep?
A) A woolly vegetable.
B) A sheep that rounds itself up.
C) A baa-ad dog.
Where is New York?
A) Under the bed.
B) I didn't take it — I promise!
C) Still in its box because the old one's not worn out yet.
How long are your legs?
A) Long enough to reach the ground.
B) Shorter than that.
C) Two weeks.

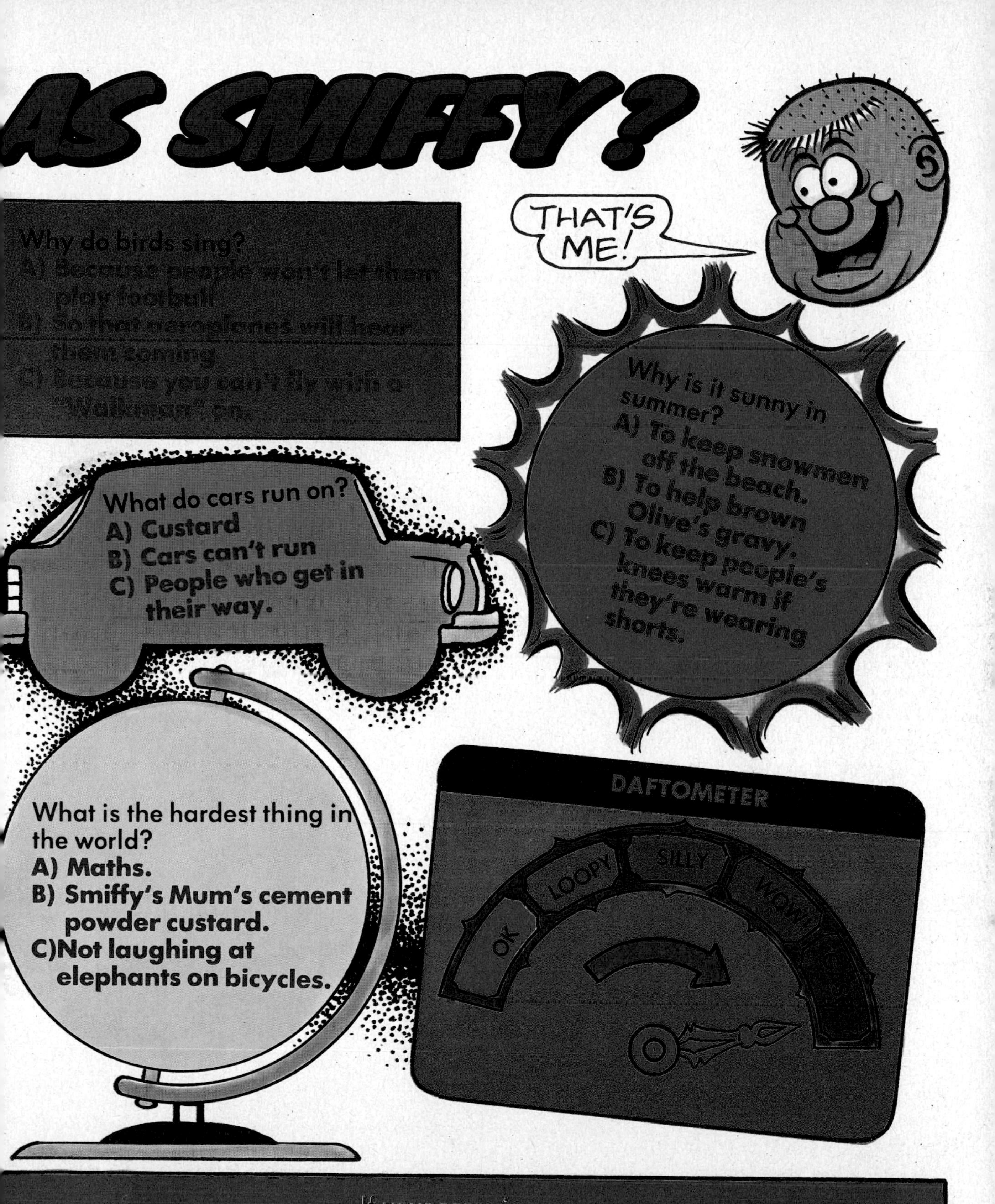

Now add up your score to see if you are as daft as Smiffy. Give yourself 1 for an (A), 2 for a (B), 3 for a (C).

If your score is
Less than 9 — You've missed a question — idiot.
9-18 — At least you can count.
15,487-90,233 — You have totally flipped.
A sausage — You need medical help and your name's probably Smiffy.

CALAMITY JAMES
SIGH! WILL I EVER BE LUCKY, ALEXANDER?
GLOOM!
FEELING EVEN MORE MISERABLE THAN USUAL!
HMM! WELL . . .
MUMPLE! GRUMP!
MILK
TRUDGE! MOPE!
. . . NO! HA-HA!
HOOT! SNORT!
FLIP!
HOWL!
TRIP!
PRAANG! JAG!
UNDERPANT-SHREDDING RRR-R-RIPP!
MUM'S MEGA-THORNY ROSE
TIP! WHIRR!
TEN TONS OF 'BEST IRISH PEAT' AS ORDERED. CARE TO SIGN FOR IT, WEE FELLER?
STINKY STUFF SERVICES LTD
one huge dollop of squelchy brown guff as ordered
OKAY!
SPLUTTER! SPLOIT! YECHHH!
SPLATTER! SQUIMPH!
HORRIBLY CLAMMY OOZINGS!

VAROOM!
HELP!
STAGNANT STEAM!
MUFFLED SQUAWKS AND SQUIRMINGS DEEP WITHIN THE SQUELCHY DEPTHS!
TWAANG! PYOINNG! NAANGLE! WHAANG!
KNICKER-ELASTIC TESTING SHEDS
HO-HUM! I SUPPOSE I'D BETTER HAUL HIM OUT!
SPACE ALIENS KEPT ME IN A JAM JAR AND LAUGHED AT MY CARDIGAN
PILCHARD FLAVOUR YOGHURT
SLOO! BELCH!
LEMMING MERINGUE PIE
FIZZY LEMMING JUICE
SU-U-UCK! SHLURRP!
SLOOBLE! BLURP!
HADDOCK SOUP
THANKS FOR PULLING ME OUT, ALEX!
EH? I DIDN'T — I WAS JUST ABOUT TO DIG YOU OUT! WHO'S THAT?
BAARP!
BIRDSEED FLAVOUR FIZZ
SHPLURT! STAGGER!
SPLEURGE! SQUENCH!
CHUG! SCOOP!
AH . . . TO BE SURE . . . YOU'VE CAUGHT ME! I WAS ASLEEP IN MY PEAT BOG BACK HOME IN IRELAND — NEXT THING YOU'RE PULLING ME OUT OF IT!
SLIGO ROVERS FOREVERMORE
GOBSMACKED GOGGLE!
HE'S AN IRISH LEPRECHAUN!
TO BE FAIR I'LL GRANT YOU ONE WISH IF YOU'LL LET ME GO!
A WISH!
OH, BOY! I COULD BE RICH!

FURTIVE WHISPER!
I WANT TO BE LUCKY!
GRAB! CLAMP! MMUMPHLE! MMMMPHH!
LITTLE HOLEY UNDERPANTS REVOLVING WITH EXCITEMENT!
TO BE SURE THAT'S AN EASY ONE TO DO!
MYSTICAL WAFFLINGS!
TIPPY-TAPPY! CLICKETTY-CLICK! CLACKY-CLACK!
JIGITTY-JIG!
WONKO-FAZONKO!
WOW!
FLAASH!
SHAZAAM!
TITTER! WISH GRANTED BUT . . .
GUFFAW-PHWAW-HAW-HAW!
HUMMM!
POOO!
PONG!
STENCH!
NIFF!
. . . SOME OF THE PEAT MUST HAVE BEEN IN THE LEPRECHAUN'S EARS! HE DIDN'T QUITE HEAR JAMES'S WISH PROPERLY! HO-HO!
WHY ANYONE WOULD WISH TO BE 'MUCKY' I'LL NEVER KNOW! TO BE SURE IT'S A FUNNY OLD WORLD!
STINK!
UMPTEEN GALLONS OF FINELY-MATURED SMELLY BROWN STUFF FROM FARMER PEABODY'S PONGIEST POOEY PIGSTY!
PERFUMED PROBOSCIS PROTECTOR
SPLUNGE! GLEURGLE! FLOUNDER! THRASH!
SKIP!
JIG!
PRANCE!

THE GERMS
GUIDE TO ILLNESS
CHICKENPOX
Ill Will's having a doze in a field —
LET'S SCATTER SOME CORN ON WILL.
HAVE A FEED, CHICKEN.
So —
WAH! I'VE CAUGHT CHICKENPOX!
CURE — Wear a horror mask when you go to sleep.

SCARLET FEVER
A WALK IN THE COUNTRY SHOULD BE HEALTHY.
AHA! A BULL! THEY HATE THE COLOUR RED.
SO LET'S PAINT WILL RED.
SNORT!
WAH!
CURE — Land in a duck pond!
WOW! MY SCARLET FEVER'S GONE!
Mirror that Will always carries to check his complexion.

HEARTBURN
YUM! I LOVE CHOC ICES!
W-WE DON'T! T-TOO C-COLD!
WHAT WILL I DO WITH THE WRAPPER?
WE'LL HAVE IT.
IT'LL WARM US UP!
OO! DREADFUL HEARTBURN!
CURE — A nice glass of milk.
BAH!

WIND
AHA! WILL'S EATING LETTUCE AND SPAGHETTI!
So—
WE'LL MAKE KITES.
GROO! I'VE GOT DREADFUL WIND!
CURE — One large burp!
BURP!
TSK! TSK!

The BEANO BIRDS
WE BIRDS LOVE IT WHEN HUMANS HANG OUT A BAG OF NUTS FOR US.
Ball Boy Bird
PUNCH!
DENNIS BIRD USES IT AS A PUNCHBAG.
DODGE BOOK
SWING!
IVY BIRD USES IT AS A SWING.
BUT I'VE GOT A MUCH BETTER USE FOR IT.
TOOL SHED
And —
THERE!
SNIP!
I'VE GOT LOTS OF 'FOOTBALLS' TO PLAY WITH . . .
KICK!
. . . AND BRILLIANT GOALNETS TO KICK INTO.
KICK!

A Daftness of NAMES
COLLECTIVE NAMES FOR GROUPS OF ANIMALS ARE OFTEN QUITE STRANGE. SEE IF YOU CAN GUESS WHAT THE FOLLOWING GROUPS OF ANIMAL ARE CALLED — I'VE DONE THE FIRST ONE FOR YOU TO GET YOU STARTED! ANSWERS AT THE FOOT OF THE NEXT PAGE.
3. A.... OF ELKS
ROAR-RR
YERK!
LEAP
6. A...... OF GOATS
HOW!

1. AN UNKINDNESS OF RAVENS
LOOK AT THE SIZE OF HIS NOSE!
YOU'RE REALLY UGLY!
POO! WHAT A SMELL!
2. A ..... OF MALLARD
PULL
GURGLE
AHEM!
4. A .... OF FALCONS
BORED
YAWN!
OUTDOOR THEATRE
Hamlet
5. A .... OF TOADS
A .... OF FERRETS
FINANCIAL CENTRE →
FINANCIAL
SHARES
GASP!
Answers
2. A FLUSH OF MALLARD
3. A GANG OF ELKS
4. A CAST OF FALCONS
5. A KNOT OF TOADS
6. A TRIBE OF GOATS
7. A BUSINESS OF FERRETS

LOOK, PUDDING, IT'S YOUR OLD PORKER PAL–
RASHER
WHY DO PIGS HAVE CURLY TAILS, RASHER?
Little Kevin — a keen Beano reader.
WATCH AND YOU'LL SEE.
POP
READY, RASHER?
POP
JAB!
COO! JUST LIKE A CORKSCREW.
TWIST!

HAVE SOME FOR YOUR HELP, RASHER.
Next —
WHY DO PIGS HAVE TUSKS?
GRR! CAN'T REACH THE BIT I WANT TO SCRATCH.
SCRITCH!
SCRATCH!
AH! THAT'S BETTER!
Then —
HAVE THESE MOULDY CHOCOLATE DROPS FOR YOUR HELP.
OO! LOVELY!
WHY DO PIGS HAVE BRISTLES?

And—
RUB AGAINST MY SHED, RASHER.
YOUR BRISTLES MAKE GREAT SANDPAPER.
RUB
PAINT
CLEVER — VERY CLEVER!
HAVE A REWARD.
FOOSTY CABBAGES — DELIGHTFUL!
HEY, RASHER. WHY . . .
NOT AGAIN!
. . . CAN'T I HAVE A CURLY TAIL, TUSKS AND BRISTLES LIKE YOU?
HOINK! HOINK! HOINK!

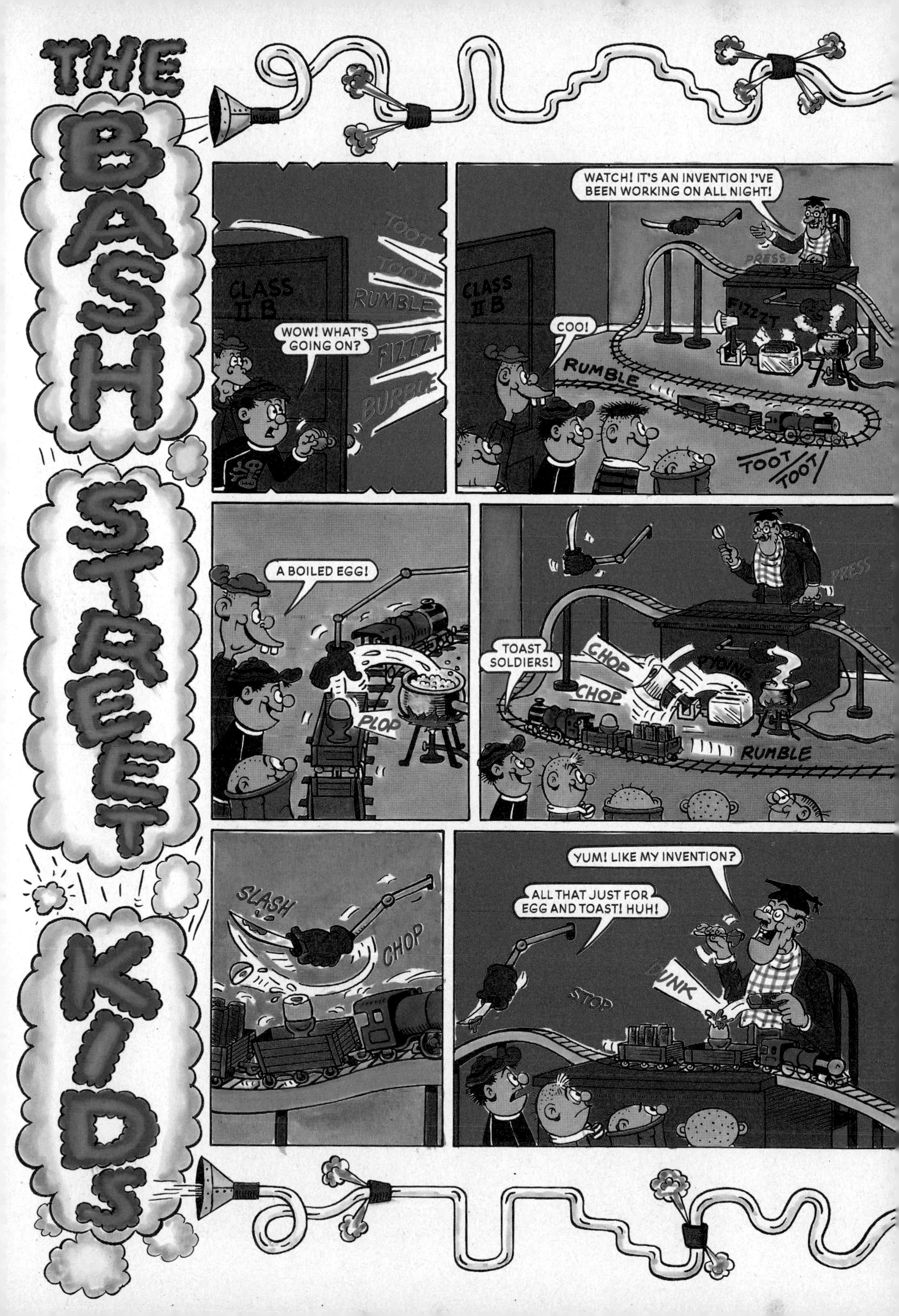
THE BASH STREET KIDS
CLASS II B
TOOT
TOOT
RUMBLE
FIZZZT
BURBLE
WOW! WHAT'S GOING ON?
WATCH! IT'S AN INVENTION I'VE BEEN WORKING ON ALL NIGHT!
CLASS II B
PRESS
COO!
FIZZZT
RUMBLE
TOOT
TOOT
A BOILED EGG!
PLOP
PRESS
TOAST SOLDIERS!
CHOP
CHOP
PYOING
RUMBLE
SLASH
CHOP
YUM! LIKE MY INVENTION?
ALL THAT JUST FOR EGG AND TOAST! HUH!
DUNK
STOP

CHOMP! BUT IT'S ONLY TO DEMONSTRATE WHAT CAN BE DONE! I WANT TO ENTER AN INVENTION OF YOURS IN A 'YOUNG INVENTORS OF THE YEAR COMPETITION'!
UH?
HAW-HAW!
SLURP
GET STARTED! THERE ARE ALL KINDS OF THINGS TO USE OVER THERE! BURP!
OKAY! LET'S START!
DAB
Later —
AHA! SYNTHETIC SNOW! ONE COULD SKI ON THIS ALL YEAR ROUND!
LIFT
NO, SIR . . .
SQUEEZE
SPLURT
SQUIRT
. . . IT'S A 'FATTY ICE-CREAM SPECIAL' I'VE MADE! CHOMP!
SPLUNGE
Next —
WE'VE MADE AN ALL WEATHER PROTECTION SUIT, SIR! WE'LL DEMONSTRATE!
SOUNDS GOOD!
HOOK
SHORTS . . . ONE WELLINGTON . . . LIGHTWEIGHT VEST . . . HALF AN UMBRELLA . . . ONE GLOVE . . . PART OF A FUR COAT . . .

NNNGH! VERY GOOD, BOYS!
CLASS IIB
CLUMP
CLUMP
BUT I CAN'T GET OUTSIDE TO TEST IT!
SIGH! BACK TO THE DRAWING BOARD!
BUMP
STUCK
Then —
I SAY, CUTHBERT! I THOUGHT YOU WOULD HAVE COME UP WITH SOMETHING A BIT BETTER THAN AN OLD WARDROBE!
SCREW
I HAVE — STEP INSIDE! ALL OF YOU!
EH? NOT ALL IN THERE!
Inside the wardrobe.
EH? BUT HOW?
EASY! LOOK OVER HERE!
HERE'S THE CENTRE OF MY INVENTION. I'VE MADE A TIME MACHINE!
COO! WRONG TIME ON THAT SUN DIAL!
IT SHOULD BE 36 O'CLOCK BY NOW, CUTHBERT!
NO . . . NO! DON'T TOUCH!
SPIN
Suddenly —
WHAT'S GOING ON?
TIME TRAVEL, SIR! I CAN'T TELL WHERE WE'LL GO BECAUSE SMIFFY'S PULLED THE HANDS OFF THE TIME SETTING CLOCK!
WAA! LET US OFF THIS MERRY-GO-ROUND!

SCREECH TO HALT
CLONK
ZONK
HMM! I WONDER WHAT TIME ZONE WE'VE LANDED IN?
LET'S SEE WHERE WE ARE!
Then —
BACK TO WORK, SLAVES!
WOW! A DRUID SLAVE DRIVER!
DOESN'T HE LOOK LIKE THE HEAD-MASTER?
MOVE IT!
NNNNGH! NOTHING EVER CHANGES!
DRAG
DRAG
Then —
DING! DING! DING!
WHAT NOW?
OOO . . . WORSE THAN WORK . . .

. . . IT'S LUNCH TIME ! GROO!
YIKES! I'M OFF!
ZIP
THROW
OLIVUS
GRUB
CLONK
GLOOP!
YEUCH! HORRIBLE!
At rest time —
HMM! I WONDER!
PLANS
HOUSE
TIPTOE
OVER THERE . . . THAT STONE GOES OVER THERE! HURRY UP!
DRAG
TUG
TUG
Much later —
OO . . . DEAR! WHAT HAVE YOU DONE, DANNY?
A FEW CHANGES TO HIS HOUSE PLANS, SIR!
HA-HA! WE HAD TO DO SOMETHING! FOOTBALL PITCHES HAVEN'T BEEN INVENTED YET! CHUCKLE!
YAHOO!
BOOT
SO THAT'S WHY STONEHENGE WAS BUILT! HMM!
SNARL! NOTHING LIKE THE HOUSE IN THE PLANS, HEAD SLAVE DRIVER!
ER . . . NO, BOSS!
TIME TO LEAVE, KIDS!
OPEN

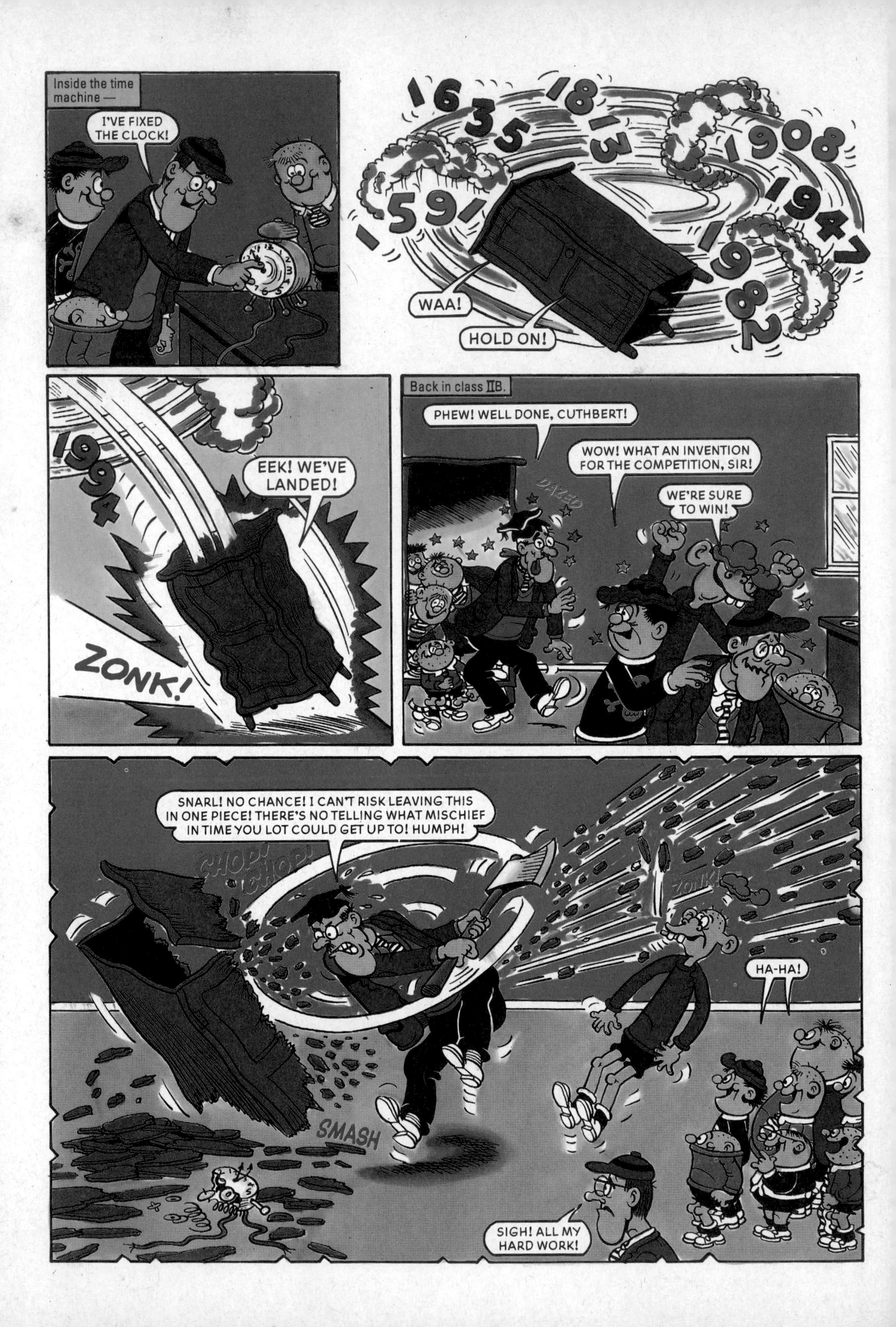
Inside the time machine —
I'VE FIXED THE CLOCK!
1635
1813
1908
1947
1982
1591
WAA!
HOLD ON!
1994
EEK! WE'VE LANDED!
ZONK!
Back in class IIB.
PHEW! WELL DONE, CUTHBERT!
WOW! WHAT AN INVENTION FOR THE COMPETITION, SIR!
WE'RE SURE TO WIN!
DAZED
SNARL! NO CHANCE! I CAN'T RISK LEAVING THIS IN ONE PIECE! THERE'S NO TELLING WHAT MISCHIEF IN TIME YOU LOT COULD GET UP TO! HUMPH!
CHOP! CHOP!
ZONK!
HA-HA!
SMASH
SIGH! ALL MY HARD WORK!

WHO ON EARTH'S THIS?

I'M MADE UP FROM 9 BEANO CHARACTERS. CAN YOU SPOT WHICH ONES? (ANSWER AT FOOT OF PAGE.)

YOU CAN SEE THE **COMPLETE** COMIC STARS IN

THE BEANO

EVERY WEEK OF THE YEAR!

ANSWERS

INK
GNERK!